D1590518

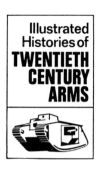

Illustrated
Histories of
**TWENTIETH
CENTURY
ARMS**

RUSSIAN INFANTRY WEAPONS
OF WORLD WAR II

1. *Soviet soldiers in the field, equipped with the 82mm Mortar M1941 with wheels dismounted for firing.*

RUSSIAN INFANTRY WEAPONS OF WORLD WAR II

by

A. J. BARKER and JOHN WALTER

ARCO PUBLISHING COMPANY, INC
New York

Published by ARCO PUBLISHING COMPANY, INC.,
219 Park Avenue South, New York, N.Y.10003
Library of Congress Catalog Card Number 72–120906
Arco Book Number 668–0 2336–8

Printed in Great Britain

Contents

Acknowledgements

The Publisher and the authors wish to express their thanks to those people who assisted in the production of this book. Special mention must be made of Herb Woodend and the staff of the Pattern Room, Royal Small Arms Factory, Enfield Lock; John Milsom; Ian Hogg; Major a. D. Hans-Rudolf von Stein; Gordon Conway; Fred Brown and Freddie Alderslade, whose excellent photographs appear in these pages.

The photographs of the weapons were specially taken at Enfield Lock by permission of the Director, Inspectorate of Armaments, to whom we wish to acknowledge our gratitude. Plate 40 appears by courtesy of Wallis & Wallis, and Plates 75-86 by courtesy of Gordon Conway.

Introduction

The Red Army

When the Red Army was created in February 1918 the Soviet leaders attempted to formulate a theory of war based on Marxism. It was intended that this theory should be different from the doctrine of the so-called Imperialist powers and aligned to the political thought of the new and growing Soviet State; but the revolutionary leaders lacked knowledge and experience of the higher conduct of war and this they tried to remedy by a study of German military works. A very large number of officers who had previously served in the Imperial Russian Army were re-employed and these officers brought with them the traditions and theories of the Tsarist General Staff. Many of them later attained very high rank and their ideas had considerable influence on the equipment, organisation and tactics of the Red Army of 1939–45.

In November 1939 the Soviet Union invaded Finland and the Red Army's inefficient performance quickly showed, among other things, that its equipment was of poor quality. Senior officers were purged and a reorganisation was initiated. The huge, unwieldy rifle division, the basic infantry formation, was reduced from 19,000 to 14,500 men and steps were taken to improve both the quality and quantity of equipment. In June 1941, however, before the reorganisation had been completed, the Germans invaded Russia and the Red Army was driven back by the well trained and better equipped Wehrmacht. Fortunately for the Russians Hitler, like Napoleon before him, had over-reached himself, and with the advent of winter the advance of the German armies was brought to a halt.

Another reorganisation of the Red Army then took place and the strength of the rifle divisions suffered a further cut. At the same time strenuous efforts were made to speed up the delivery of new and better equipment. Approximately 12 'Fronts'—equivalent to British and American Army Groups—were formed, each composed of three rifle armies, one tank army and one air army. When two or more fronts were involved in an operation (as at Stalingrad) a command team was sent from Moscow to co-ordinate their operations. Throughout the war the main strength of the Red Army lay in its numbers: by VE Day it had suffered 13 million killed or permanently disabled, while the German forces confronting it suffered less than one third of that number of similar casualties. Despite such an astronomically high casualty rate the Russian troops on the European front in the final phases of the war still outnumbered the Germans opposing them by over two to one.

Rifle armies usually contained three rifle corps, each of three rifle divisions, and the backbone of such divisions were their rifle regiments. Similarly a tank army contained a large proportion of mechanised infantry whose organisation was similar to that of the rifle division. In the latter the rifleman normally marched and most of the transport was horse-drawn. Divisions were commanded by major-generals, regiments by colonels, battalions by lieutenant-colonels or majors, companies by captains and platoons by lieutenants. War establishment strength of a rifle division was about 9,000, that of a rifle regiment about 2,000 and each of the three rifle companies in a battalion totalled nominally 110. At full strength this company had three sections of 9 men each making up three platoons of 30; additionally every rifle company had a machine-gun platoon of 16 men, divided into three sections with one medium machine-gun each—usually the ubiquitous Maxim, or the SG after 1943.

Also included in the rifle battalion organisation was a medium machine-gun company of three platoons organised on similar lines to the machine-gun platoons of the rifle companies. A mortar company (of three mortar platoons each of three sections with five men in per section serving a medium mortar) and an artillery battery completed the battalion commander's support weapons group. Much of the organisation described so far was similar to that of both the other allies and the axis armies. Only the artillery battery may be considered unique. It comprised a battalion 'gun' troop, an anti-aircraft gun troop of four 12·7mm heavy machine guns and an anti-tank troop with four outmoded anti-tank rifles. Signals, medical and supply platoons completed the battalion organisation.

There is no doubt about the quality of the Soviet troops, particularly the Red Army's infantrymen: brave in the attack, stubborn in defence, the Russian soldier appeared to set little value on his life. Little more than twenty years after the Revolution the Russian peasant was accustomed to a hard life and expected little from it—in this respect his character had undergone little change since the Crimean war. His upbringing had taught him self-reliance and the resourcefulness to live frugally as well as the importance of im-provisation: propaganda had taught him to fight bitterly and ruthlessly. Nevertheless he was neither so brave, tough or frugal as the Japanese, nor did he have the general technical ability and education of the American, British or German soldier.

Equipment
Reference has already been made to the fact that the Soviet Union entered the war against Germany with equipment of a very much lower standard than the Germans. However, as a result of a clear appreciation of what was needed and a great design and production effort, within two years she was able to manufacture weapons of a standard equal—and in some case superior—to those of her allies and Germany. This was especially noticeable in the case of tanks and artillery. Simple design and robust construction were the guiding principles, and although the Red Army's weapons often seemed rough and very conventional they were effective and often impressive. By the end of the war the armament and armour of Russian tanks might be said to have been the best in the world, and Russian artillery was the equal of the Germans (Russia having been artillery minded even in Tsarist times). But the development of infantry weapons seems to have been regarded as of secondary importance and so her standard weapons could be summarized as being orthodox, of no outstanding merit and in many cases of obsolete design. (This was not true for mortars, which were seen as artillery and the Russians were alone among the great powers in developing a heavy mortar.) The reason for this was deep-seated in history. To a large degree the nature of Soviet military smallarms was determined by the evolution of the smallarms industry in Imperial Russia. Like the United States, the Tsar's Russia relied on French smallarms leadership, and this dependence continued until the time of the Crimean war. Throughout the eighteenth and nineteenth centuries the Russians were developing their eastern frontier like the Americans in the west. But no great private smallarms industries like Colt, Remington or Winchester appeared and there was no government development like Enfield. The demands of the Imperial Armies were satisfied by purchases abroad or by the Tula, Izhevsk and Sestroretsk Arsenals, which copied foreign patterns. This situation continued until 1883 when the part-Belgian part-Russian M1891 rifle was selected for adoption. (Soviet historians contend that government agents received such large fees from foreign arms concerns that the development of an indigenous smallarms industry always met with strong opposition. Whether this is true or not, it is a fact that the Imperial Army failed to include Colonel Mosin's name in the official designation of the rifle, and that the first orders for it were placed with the French Government's Chatellerault Arsenal.) Not until the scandalous shortages in World War I did the Imperial Government recognize the smallarms problem—and by then time was running out. How the new Revolutionary government tackled the problem is explained in the following pages.

9

Pistols and Revolvers

The first service revolver pattern to be issued on a large scale to the Russian forces was the Smith & Wesson 'Russian Model' of 1872, the inventors' firm supplying 150,000 of the revolvers to the Imperial Russian government during the period 1872–7; it is ironical that the Russian authorities ordered 70,000 further guns from the firm of Ludwig Loewe and Company of Berlin in 1878, the year following the completion of the Smith and Wesson contracts—the Loewe guns were replicas of the American design, made in defiance of the patent arrangements. They were also cheaper.

In the early 1890s the Russians decided to adopt a weapon of smaller calibre than the 0·44in Smith & Wesson, and eventually settled on the design of the Nagant brothers of Belgium. This weapon, which had been invented by Emile and Leon Nagant in 1893, incorporated a 'gas seal' feature which, though not a new idea, was at its most effective in this design. In operation the cylinder slid forward over a rearward extension of the barrel, the ammunition being contained in a long brass cartridge that protruded into the barrel at the moment of firing. At discharge the neck of the case expanded and momentarily sealed the slight gap between bore and chamber. This feature was fairly effective; when the standard Nagant ball cartridge was fired in revolvers of differing barrel lengths, some with the seal and others without, the results were as follows—a 5·5in barrel with the seal in use gave a velocity of 1,082fps while without the seal a value of 725fps was obtained. An 11·8in 'sealed' barrel registered a velocity of 1,394fps, while without the seal the velocity was raised by a mere 30fps to 755.

The Russian authorities also bought a limited quantity of the improved Nagant revolver of 1910, provided with a cylinder which swung out to the left for loading, thus overcoming the biggest drawback of the M1895. These weapons were marked as the products of Fabrique d'Armes et d'Automobiles Nagant Frères of Liège in Belgium. The Nagant M1895 design was produced in quantity at the Tula Arsenal as well as at the Nagant workshops in Liège. (Specimens from Tula have been noted with dates as late as 1943, but no Belgian-made Nagant appears to have been made after 1913–4.) Two versions were manufactured—in double-action form for the officers and single-action for the NCOs and enlisted men. The Nagant proved to be quite acceptable to the Russians and little was done to find a replacement until 1928–30, although the authorities had meanwhile obtained a small quantity of the M1898 Schwarzlose self-loading pistol; these were bought in Germany by the 1905 Revolutionaries, seized by the Imperial authorities and later issued to the Tsarist police. Larger numbers of the Mauser M1896 design were also purchased as officers' weapons.

In the late 1920s, the designer Fedor Tokarev offered the Soviet authorities a modified and much simplified variation of the Browning principles embodied in the Colt M1911 pistol; this was immediately accepted and placed in limited production as the TT1930 (TT representing Tula-Tokarev). A modified version of this weapon, the TT1933, replaced the earlier type on the production lines. Also about this time a small officer's defence weapon was introduced, called the TK or Tula-Korovin, but this was never authorised as service issue. Two small-calibre variations of the Tokarev design appeared in 1935–7: the TTR3, a training weapon, employed blowback principles of operation, using the 5·56mm (0·22in Long Rifle) cartridge and outwardly resembling the TT1933. The TTR4, meanwhile, was a target pistol with the mechanism of the TTR3 (and hence the external appearance of the full-bore Tokarev) but with an extended barrel. Nothing like the enormous quantity of the full-bore pistols claimed to have been made by the Russians were actually produced—largely because of the ever increasing use of the machine carbine—and in relation to these weapons the Tokarev remained rather scarce.

11

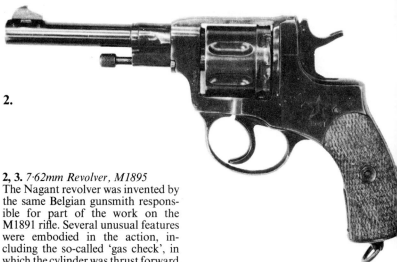

2.

2, 3. *7·62mm Revolver, M1895*
The Nagant revolver was invented by
the same Belgian gunsmith respons-
ible for part of the work on the
M1891 rifle. Several unusual features
were embodied in the action, including the so-called 'gas check', in
which the cylinder was thrust forward
over the rear extension of the barrel
to provide a reasonably efficient gas
seal; to make full use of this feature,
the revolver's cartridge, of unusual
design, had the bullet seated completely in the cartridge case. The case
neck extended forward of the bullet
and, on discharge, momentarily expanded to form a seal between
cylinder and barrel. This feature
apart, the Nagant was a relatively
standard revolver in appearance,
having an under-barrel ejection rod
which swung out to the right and was
then pushed rearwards through the
chambers to eject the fired cases. No
return spring was provided to bear
on this rod, which had to be operated
entirely by hand, making the re-
loading of the seven chambers a
somewhat tedious process. The
revolvers were issued in two forms, a
double action type intended for
officers, and a single action for the
other ranks. M1895 revolvers were
produced both in Belgium (1895–
1913) and Russia (c. 1900–1943).

4. *7·62mm Automatic Pistols, TT1930
and TT1933*
The original pistols of this type were
introduced for trials in 1930, and a
slightly modified version was adopted

for official use in 1933. Initial issue
seems to have been on a limited
scale, few Tokarev pistols having
been captured from the Russians
during the Russo-Finnish War of
1939–40, although more specimens
were captured during the later campaigns. The Tokarev was essentially
a modified and simplified version of
the Colt-Browning pistol design, although the Russian derivation had,
despite inferior workmanship, several
superior design features when com-
pared with the original patents. The
two Soviet models differed only in
minor details, the barrel lugs of the
TT1930 were identical to those of the
Colt M1911, but those of the TT1933
were machined completely around
the circumference of the barrel to
permit easier manufacture. The dis-
connector (a mechanical device to
prevent fully automatic fire) surfaces
were enlarged on the later model. No
provision was made for any safety
devices save for a half-cock notch
on the hammer; the grips of the pistol
were either plain walnut or grooved
plastic bearing a device consisting of
the encircled letters CCCP. Despite
the relative crudity of these weapons
they were as efficiently lethal as the
most expensive commercial pistols.

12

3.

4.

5.

5. *5·56mm Automatic Pistol, TTR4*
This pistol was essentially similar in external appearance to the TT automatic designs in 7·62 calibre. It was issued as a target weapon, fired the 0·22in Long Rifle cartridge and carried adjustable sights.

6. *6·35mm Automatic Pistol, TK*
This little blowback operated pistol was never officially recognised, attaining the sole status of a privately bought weapon intended for the personal defence of staff officers; despite this, however, a rumour persisted that it was much loved by the police and the KGB on account of its small size.

6.

Rifles

By 1890 the Russian authorities had come to the conclusion that a new rifle design would be needed if their armies were to be the equal of those of the other major European Powers and, as a result of extensive trials, they decided to adopt the M1891 rifle designed by their own Colonel Sergei Ivanovich Mosin and the Nagant brothers of Liège. The Tsarist arms industry was not equipped for the volume production of such weapons, and so the initial contracts were placed abroad, the rifles being made in France (by the Imperial Manufactory at Chatellerault) in Switzerland (by Schweizerische Industrie Gesellschaft at Neuhausen-am-Rheinfalls), and in Austria (by Österreichische Waffenfabrik at Steyr); the weapons made in Switzerland and at Steyr are perhaps the most attractively finished of all the Russian types. Before these contracts had expired, however, the Russians found that they had reached the stage where they were capable of producing some of the weapons for themselves, and indigenous production started at the arsenals of Tula and Sestroretsk in 1894–5.

With the onset of World War I, the Russian centres were ill-equipped to deal with the demands for weapons coming from the front: the Tsarist Government reacted to the crisis by placing emergency contracts with the American arms concern of Winchester, who made M1895 lever action rifles for the Russians in 1915–6, and also with Remington and the New England Westinghouse Company (both of whom made M1891 rifles). Few of these were delivered to the Tsarist and Kerensky régimes before an embargo was placed on deliveries of weapons to Revolutionary Russia.

Ostensibly the Russians were eminently satisfied with the performance of their M1891 rifle which, they said, had operated reliably in conditions ranging from the extreme cold of the Artic zone to the arid wastes of Turkestan; the only disadvantages lay in the cumbersome length of the weapon and its slow rate of aimed fire. Despite the apparent success of the weapon, however, several attempts were made to provide a suitable self-loading weapon for the Russian forces as an ultimate replacement; most of the early designs were naturally based on the parts of the service rifle, Vasiliy Grigorevich Federov managing to convert a Mosin-Nagant in

15

7. The M1895 Winchester lever-action rifle, chambered for the 7·62mm Russian rifle cartridge.

late 1905 and two years later another designer, Yevgeniy Roshchepei, invented an automatic rifle in which it was said that 'the barrel stood still'; this, however, barely reached the prototype stage before being abandoned. The first automatic weapon of rifle type to attain quantity production was the AVF1916 designed once again by Vasiliy Federov. The number of these weapons made has been variously estimated as being between 2,000 and 3,500, all built at the Sestroretsk plant in 1916–8. The gun operated on the short recoil principle, locking being achieved by two pivoting blocks at the rear of the barrel. The design was overcomplicated, said to have been derived in many ways from the Mauser M1896 self-loading pistol, and was consequently both difficult to manufacture and to maintain. An unusual feature of the weapon was that, rather than being chambered for the Russian 7·62mm rifle cartridge, the barrel was originally intended to take the Japanese Type 30 (Arisaka) round. The reason for this has never been satisfactorily explained—it may be that the Russian ammunition was either unsuitable or of substandard quality, or perhaps the Russians simply wanted a less powerful 'intermediate' type cartridge rather than that of the standard rifle.

When the political situation in Russia had stabilised in the mid-twenties, attempts were once again made to design a suitable self-loading rifle. Extensive trials were staged between 1929 and 1933 at the Soviet Ordance Proving Grounds (NIAP) situated at Solnechogorsk, some 75 kilometres north-west of Moscow, and at the Scientific Research Station and Proving Grounds of the Central Council of the Ossoaviakhim (NIIS OAKh) at Kuskovo, 120 kilometres east of Moscow. Many weapons were submitted for these trials, including designs by Degtyarev, Federov, Koleshnikov, Simonov and Tokarev. (Simonov's weapon was a prototype of the AVS 1936, whilst Tokarev's was the forerunner of the 1938 and 1940 service models.) As a result of these trials limited quantities of the early Simonov and Tokarev designs were made and issued to the troops, although neither proved very successful and were quickly withdrawn. They were followed by the AVS1936, a Simonov design which proved too complex, being replaced by a Tokarev weapon which was issued throughout the war to NCOs—but still fell short of perfection.

8. *7·62mm Mosin-Nagant Trials Rifle,
c. 1890*
There were several differences between the rifle illustrated (which is one of the rare experimental models of 1889–90) and the production variety, particularly with regard to the action (where the differences will be better seen in Plate 11). The bolt handle did not lock down in front of the receiver bridge as in the later type, and the cocking piece and the bolt guide rib were of considerably different design. The magazine, too, showed much modification for the final model and a small finger rest appeared behind the trigger guard. The weapon was provided with a bayonet of slightly differing proportions to the standard type and possessing a differently cut locking mortise. It is assumed that the rifles were made in Liège, either by Nagant themselves or by a contractor, the weapon itself yielding no clue as to the place of manufacture.

9. *7·62mm Rifle, M1891*
This was the finalised rifle design chosen to equip the Tsar's Armies, and it remained the Russian infantryman's basic weapon until 1930. The initial production runs were without the characteristic wooden handguard on top of the barrel and were provided with sling swivels rather than the later slots, cut through the stock although the trigger guard design remained the same throughout. One sling swivel was placed in front of the magazine housing and the other appeared underneath the top barrel band. All weapons made prior to the 1917 Revolution had the sights graduated in arshins, a Russian term representing one pace (equivalent to 0·711 metres, or 27·99in). Those made after October 1917—or having undergone major repair to the sights after that time—were graduated in metres, as the new regime had by that time adopted the metric system. All the M1891 rifles were provided with the long obsolete M1891 design of socket bayonet with a locking ring (although the later bayonet with the spring catch, the M1891/30 was interchangeable). Mosin rifles were sometimes fitted with a bayonet lug on the barrel—a steel collar secured to the barrel by two small screws indicated that the rifle had been captured from the Russians and had seen emergency use with the German forces during World War I. An integral lug indicated one of the Finnish derivatives which used a knife bayonet. A Gewehr 98-style bayonet bar meant that the rifle was a Polish modification to the basic type. Some of these weapons were later shortened by the Soviets to conform to the length of the M1891/30.

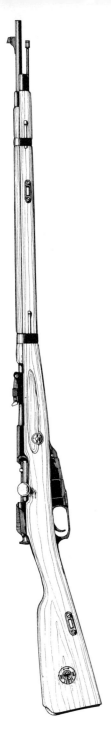

Above. Two typical stock marks found on weapons of the Imperial era.

10. *7·62 Dragoon Rifle, M1891*
The so-called Dragoon Rifle, issued to the Tsar's mounted troops, *c.* 1900, was essentially similar to the original M1891 rifle, with a hexagonal receiver, and a barrel some three inches shorter than the basic weapon for easier shooting from the saddle. The sling slots were cut through the stock and the normal pattern of wooden handguard appeared over the barrel. The M1891 socket bayonet was originally issued with these weapons, although the later M1891/30 type was interchangeable and was sometimes substituted by the Soviets. Owing to the still considerable overall length, the Dragoon Rifle was supplemented by the M1910 carbine (although the later weapon never entirely replaced it).

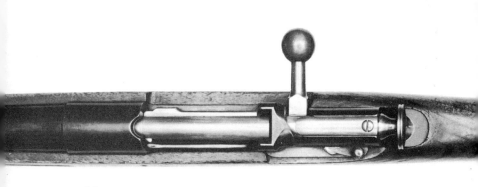

11.

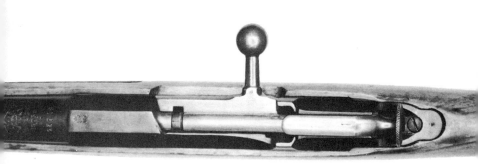

12.

11, 12. *Comparison of the actions of the Trials and M1891 rifles*

This view clearly shows the differences between the original trials gun (plate 11) and the standard Imperial rifle (plate 12), this specimen being made at the Sestroretsk Arsenal. The most noticeable changes concerned the receiver design and the positioning of the bolt handle which, in the former case, locked down behind the clip guide—itself an integral part of the receiver. In the later weapon the bolt handle locked down in front of the receiver bridge in standard Mannlicher practice. In the normal M1891, the guide rib was an integral part of the bolt handle, and also provided an added safety factor where it abutted the receiver wall when locked: in the earlier weapon there was no such provision. The general shape of the receiver body and the cocking piece also displayed marked dissimilarities, and the Trials model (of which it is thought that about 1,000 were made) had a cylindrical receiver. It is interesting to note that the Soviets later returned to a receiver design of cylindrical form in the interests of simplyifying manufacture.

13. *Rearsights*

The sight on the right was the standard Russian Imperial type, the accompanying M1891 rifle being manufactured at the Sestroretsk Arsenal in 1905: the sight was a conventional leaf pattern, with the sight bed graduated from 200–1000 arshins in steps of 200, and the graduations continuing on the leaf to 2600 arshins in progressions of 100. A V notch was provided in the top of the leaf to give the maximum sighting distance of 2700 arshins (1822 yards), and the slider was unlocked by depressing the two buttons on either side. The middle weapon was one of the 840,307 rifles made by Remington for Russia, the sights were essentially similar to the preceding type, but the rearsight was a little larger and the leaf was graduated to 3200 arshins without the V notch. The sight on the left was the Soviets' tangent variety for the M1891/30, this particular weapon being made at Tula in 1938, and was graduated from 100–2000 metres in steps of 100. The sight is shown in a raised position: when in a firing attitude, the slider rested against the inclined sides of the sight base.

14. *7·62mm Carbine, M1910*
This was the first Russian attempt to provide a shortened version of the basic rifle design for issue as a carbine. The issue was extremely limited, and it was manufactured for less than seven years, production ceasing with the 1917 Revolution. However it was this carbine which served as a prototype for the Soviet 1938 pattern. There was still the Tsarist era's hexagonal receiver and sling slots rather than swivels, but the rearsight was graduated only to 2000 arshins (instead of 2700 or 3200 on the rifle); the stock extended forward of the top barrel band almost as far as the muzzle and, because of the lengthened stock, no bayonet could be attached to the carbine.

15. *7·62mm Rifle, M1891/30*
This was the Soviet derivative of the basic M1891 rifle, which formed the basic infantry weapon during the thirties and early years of World War II. Immediately after the Revolution, the Russians had been content merely to shorten some of the long rifles to Dragoon Rifle specifications, but in 1930 the M1891/30 rifle was introduced as a variation from the shortened weapons, the latter usually being recognisable by the hexagonal receiver and also by the weapon's date of manufacture (before 1917). The M1891/30 differs primarily from the M1891 in that the barrel was shortened to approximate to that of the Dragoon Rifle, and the section of the receiver body altered from hexagonal to circular—the change making manufacture less exacting. The foresight was changed from 'open barleycorn' (an inverted V) to a tapered post hooded by a cylindrical guard, and the old leaf rearsight was replaced by a tangent-leaf graduated in metres rather than in arshins. The design of the accompanying bayonet was modified to provide a more secure method of fixing it to the barrel, the archaic locking ring being replaced by a spring-loaded catch.

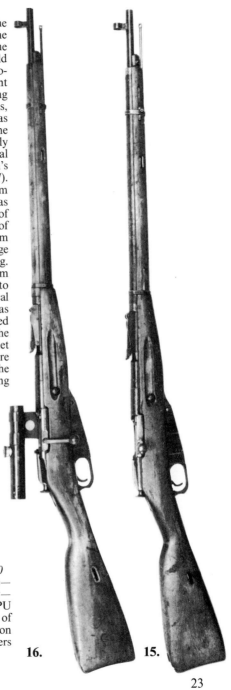

16. *7·62mm Sniper Rifle, M1891/30*
This was a standard M1891/30 rifle— usually selected for its accuracy— and was fitted with either PE or PU telescopic sights on a variety of mounts (see page 64). The weapon remained in use by Soviet snipers throughout World War II.

16.

15.

17.   18.   19.

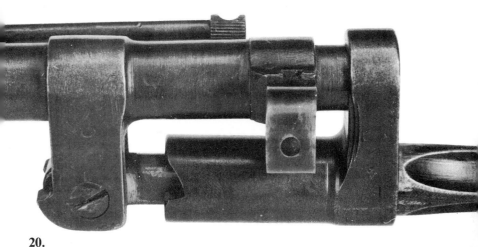

20.

17. *7·62mm Carbine, M1938*
The true carbine derivation of the
M1891/30 rifle, the M1938 was
basically similar to the earlier weapon
but with a shortened barrel, and the
old tangent-leaf rearsight (graduated
to 2,000 metres) was replaced with a
smaller version graduated to 1,000
metres. The carbine was otherwise
the same as the rifle, with protruding
box magazine, wooden handguard,
sling slots and a cleaning rod beneath
the barrel. The foresight remained a
barleycorn blade type protected by a
cylindrical guard. Manufacture of
this carbine is believed to have
started in 1938 and ceased in 1943.

18, 19, 20. *7·62mm Carbine, M1944*
The carbine design of 1944 was the
last of the long series of Mosin-
Nagant weapons to be introduced to
the Russian army. With its standard
cylindrical receiver, sling slots, and
barrel handguard this weapon was
almost identical to the preceding
carbine design, the M1938. The sights
were standardised as the 1,000 metre
tangent rearsight and the barleycorn blade foresight protected by a

cylindrical guard. The great
difference between the 1944 carbine
and its predecessors lay in the perm-
anent attachment of a folding
bayonet along the right side of the
muzzle and stock of the weapon.
The fact that this could be used only
for thrusting presented few difficulties
to the average Russian infantryman,
who invariably carried the standard
form of socket bayonet fixed any-
way, as scabbards were never issued
by the Russian authorities. The 1944
bayonet consisted of a straight cruci-
form blade terminating in a chisel
point—a standard Russian feature—
and a cylindrical steel hilt with a
muzzlering. The whole unit pivoted
around a bolt passing through a
special projection on the side of the
barrel. To set the bayonet in either
the extended or retracted positions,
the hilt was grasped and pulled for-
wards, away from the pivot, against
the tension of an internal spring: it
was then swung around until the
notch on the pivot caught in a slot in
the hilt. There appears to have been
two forms of bayonet, differing only
in the design of the catch.

22.

23.

25.

21, 22, 23. *7·62mm Automatic Rifle, AVS1936*
The AVS was a gas actuated weapon, locked by the vertical action of a hollow block sliding in grooves in the receiver. The weapon was easily recognised by the unusual muzzle brake/compensator—of doubtful effectiveness—and a large cutaway in the bolt cover to permit the retraction of the cocking handle, which was far from desirable as mud

and dust could enter the action through this port; a sliding dust cover was provided but the gap still opened when the rifle was cocked. The clearing rod was inset along the right side of the barrel (missing in the photograph along with the magazine) and the stock was a fragile two-piece design with a sheet-steel handguard protecting the forward portion. The AVS was also capable of selective fire, the selector lever appearing at

26

Above. A typical Soviet stock mark, applied in particular to the AVS1936 rifles

the right rear of the receiver. It was largely due to difficulties encountered in machining the complex mechanism, and jamming caused by débris entering the action, that the AVS was abandoned in favour of the SVT1938. A sniper version of the AVS equipped with optical sights was produced in limited quantity.

24, 25. *7·62mm Self-loading rifle, SVT1938*
All the Tokarev designed weapons in this series relied on gas operation, and a locking block cammed downwards at the rear into a recess in the receiver floor. The SVT1938 had a two-piece wooden stock with a prominent magazine; there were two steel barrel bands and the forward portion of the wooden handguard was replaced by one of sheet steel with circular cooling apertures drilled into each side. Immediately behind these, rectangular cooling slots were cut into the wooden guard. The principal distinguishing feature was the positioning of the cleaning rod, inserted along the side of the stock rather than underneath the barrel of the weapon. The rifle was originally fitted with a six-baffle muzzle brake, replaced in late 1940 or early 1941 by a two-baffle unit. Owing to its fragile construction, the SVT1938 was abandoned in 1940, but not before some selected weapons had been fitted with telescopic sights (see page 64).

21. **24.**

26.   **27.**   **28.**

26. *7·62mm Self-loading Rifle, SVT1940*
A more robust version of the 1938 Tokarev design, the SVT1940 was characterised by not having the externally mounted cleaning rod; instead this was mounted according to convention beneath the barrel. There was only a single barrel band, beyond which a sheet metal hand-guard extended forward; on the SVT1940 it was of 'wrap-around' type as opposed to the 'metal-and-wood' forward guard of the SVT 1938. Like its predecessor air circulation holes were drilled into the guard, and four rectangular slots appeared through the wooden continuation. Two variations in muzzle brake design existed: the first had six slim baffles replaced in later production by a unit having only two large baffles. These self-loading rifles were issued mainly to NCOs, although as with the SVT1938 models selected specimens were equipped with telescopic sights and issued to snipers.

A fully automatic version, called the AVT1940, was outwardly identical to the self-loading SVT1940 (from which they were converted) save for alteration to the surround of the safety catch to permit the addition of an automatic fire adjustment: however, only a very few rifles were thus converted.

27, 28. *7·62mm Self-loading Carbine, SVT1940*
Carbine modifications to the Tokarev weapons were rare indeed. Some of the 1940 design were so altered but no evidence has yet been uncovered to support the claim that some of the 1938 type were also modified. Two varieties of the 1940 carbines existed: those cut down from the original rifles (plate 27), and those actually made as carbines c.1942 (plate 28). In the modified rifles, the stock was cut away, the barrel band moved rearwards and the steel handguards greatly abbreviated. The barrel was then shortened and the weapon re-assembled to give a much more compact weapon than the original rifle; the whole appearance of the conversion suggested considerable haste, as the fit of the parts left much to be desired. Small quantities of the true carbine were made at the Soviet arsenals and were easily distinguished by the full length metal handguard. The barrels of the latter type show no signs of alteration.

Submachine-guns

In the 1930s the Soviet authorities did little to encourage the production of submachine-guns until they had equipped their armies with more urgently-needed heavy weapons. With the success of the DP light machine-gun, however, the designers were freed to work on other projects, and their efforts were turned towards a study of specimens of the German Bergmann MP18/1, the first of the submachine-gun designs to achieve any degree of success. As a result, the first Russian type—credited to the design team led by Degtyarev and called the PPD1934—bore a close resemblance to the earlier German gun. Both operated on blowback principles using what is often called the 'Bergmann System' and both fed the cartridges into the firing chamber from a spring-operated drum magazine. The PPD1934/38 was an improved version of this 1934 design, from which it differed in minor respects, including the design of the magazine. Two variations of feed unit were to be found, a drum magazine and a simpler box type with a lower capacity. The drum—characterised on this weapon by a short vertical extension to fit the feed aperture—was greatly favoured amongst the Russian troops, who were supposedly prepared to accept its excessive weight because of its greater cartridge capacity. The PPD1934/38, which appeared in three distinct sub-varieties, remained relatively scarce and was eventually supplanted on the production lines by an improved design known as the PPD1940. The latter type was designed to use many of the components of the earlier weapons which meant that they could be produced at minimum cost and without the need for extensive retooling. The principal difference between the PPD1934/38 and the PPD1940 was the magazine: the vertical feed extension was eliminated on the later model after complaints about malfeeding, the result being that the 1940 design's drum was placed noticeably higher in relation to the centre-line of the barrel than that of the PPD1934/38. Because of this, the PPD1940 used a stock that was divided at the magazine housing instead of the one-piece type of the earlier weapons. Once again the production runs were very short, a much simplified design being hastily introduced as a result of the frantic scramble to produce weapons when the Germans overran a number of the smallarms factories outside Moscow in the summer of 1941.

The new design was the work of Georgiy Shpagin (who had collaborated with Degtyarev on the design of the DShK1938 heavy machine-gun) and was known as the PPSh1941. Composed largely of unfinished pressings and stampings roughly welded together this weapon was the essence of simplicity. Manufacture bordered on crudity, but the Soviet Army was desperate for every kind of weapon that would help to stem the German advance, and so appearance counted for little. Production was often carried out in ill-equipped workshops with little or no machining facilities. The gun was inexpensive and effective, and also well suited to the Soviet strategy of attempting to halt the Germans by sheer weight of numbers, regardless of losses to men and equipment. An interesting sidelight on the design of the PPSh1941 was the use of quantities of obsolete or damaged Mosin-Nagant rifle barrels which, were cut in half to provide barrels for the submachine-guns. Sometimes their bores were often chromium plated to minimise wear. As with the Degtyarev guns, the PPSh type—which fired standard 7·62mm Tokarev pistol cartridges in common with all of the Russian weapons of this type—was supplied with two alternative types of magazine.

In 1942 a small issue of a new submachine-gun was made to selected Guards units and to the Soviet paratroops. (Guards, incidentally, were not élite regiments as in the British Army. Any infantry unit which distinguished itself in combat won the title of Guards—and lost it again if it failed to maintain the high standards required.) The new weapon was the PPS1942, designed by a little known engineer by the name of Vladimir Sudarev—the gun itself bore considerable resemblance to the German MP38 and MP40 (Schmeisser) designs used by the Wehrmacht forces on a large scale. In the following year an improved and modified version was introduced, called the PPS1943, which differed from its forerunner in several minor respects. While the Sudarev types were readily recognisable by their folding metal shoulder stock, the PPD and PPSh models retained the cumbersome wooden stock.

29.

30.

31.

29, 30. *7·62mm Submachine-gun, PPD1934/38*
Based on the Bergmann MP18/1, this was the first indigenous design to reach production status. The weapon worked on the blowback principle and was fed either from a drum magazine characterised by a vertical extension to fit the magazine aperture, or from a 25 round capacity box unit. It was distinguished from the PPD1940 by the one-piece wooden stock, and included provision for both semi- and fully-automatic fire.

Three variations in the basic M1934/38 design are known to have existed. The first had a one-piece trigger guard and a selector lever numbered 1 and 73. The barrel casing had four rows of eight rectangular slots. The second variation had a two-piece welded trigger guard with a selector lever numbered 1 and 71 on opposite sides. This weapon used the same barrel casing as the previous type. The third variant combined the guard and lever of the second type with the barrel casing of the PPD1940.

31. *7·62mm Submachine-gun, PPD 1940*
The PPD1940 Degtyarev carbine, developed from the Bergmann, continued to use the same blowback system as its forbears. In external appearance, this design was similar to the PPD1934/38 type, its chief distinguishing feature being a two-piece stock. The magazine unit, with no vertical extension, was set noticeably higher into the feed channel than that on the earlier versions, and the cooling slots in the barrel jacket were approximately twice the length of those of the original PPD1934/38. A safety catch on the bolt handle locked the bolt either in the forward or cocked position and a selector switch appeared on the trigger guard.

32, 33. *7·62mm Submachine-gun, PPSh1941*
Like the other submachine-guns, the PPSh operated on blowback principles, and was fed from a drum magazine patterned after that of the Thompson, although specimens were

33

sometimes encountered with the box type of the PPS (*q.v.*), which was a far less complex mechanism. The barrels were mainly salvaged from quantities of obsolete M1891 rifles, each rifle barrel providing two sub-machine-gun barrels; some were then chromium plated internally to mini-mise wear. The PPSh was character-ised by a wooden 'half-stock', with-out any forward handgrip: the wood, often very dense and of a yellowish hue, was sometimes coated with a clear lacquer. The barrel casing ex-tended forward of the muzzle to form a rudimentary compensator and, although provision was generally made for selective fire (some of the guns made from 1942–3 lack this capability), no safety devices were provided—with the possible except-ion of the trigger pull which, varying between 20 and 25 lb, represented a safety feature in itself. Plate 32 shows the variations in magazines and in the rearsight which, originally a tangent leaf type graduated to 500 metres, was later altered to a rocking L with positions for 100 and 200 metres.

34. *7·62mm Submachine-gun, PPS 1943*

The PPS1943 supplemented the avail-able stocks of the PPSh and the experimental PPS1942 (from which it differed mainly in having a one-piece barrel casing without a vertical joint in front of the magazine). The PPS designs were blowback operated, and showed a marked affinity with the German MP38. The feed unit on the PPS was the curved box mentioned under the PPSh, but, unlike the earlier gun, the PPS has a safety catch at the front of trigger guard. Although again composed of sheet metal pressings, the PPS was of noticeably better finish than all its predecessors and could be im-mediately recognized by the metal stock, which folded forward over the bolt housing and fitted around the rearsight. The only part of the PPS that was not metal was the grip, which was made from plastic or wood. Seven cooling holes appeared in the barrel casing to which was welded a sheet steel compensator, left with open sides.

Machine-guns

The earliest machine-guns supplied to the Russian forces were Maxim types obtained through the agencies of the Vickers' Sons & Maxim Machine Gun Company in England. By 1905, however, the Tsarist arms industry was sufficiently well established as to enable the Russians to produce sufficient weapons for their own needs, although the Tula plant had begun to produce machine-gun barrels a few years previously; the first indigenous variant was built on Maxim's principles and called the PM1905 (Pulemet Maxim, or Maxim machine-gun, Model 1905), the weapon being provided with a bronze water jacket.

During the period 1912–3, military publications began to mention a new type of Russian Maxim, referred to at this time as the PM1910 —and this weapon was to serve the Russians throughout World War II. It differed from its predecessor mainly in its substitution of a sheet-steel barrel jacket for the original bronze unit, and in a slight redesign of the feed mechanism.

Several variations on the 1910 design have been noted, and the gun, along with the equally famous 'Sokolov' mount, was used by the Soviet forces even after the introduction of the SG1943. The final version was modified from the original PM1910 by the addition of a very large water entry port to facilitate the replenishment of the coolant. An aircraft version of the PM1910, called the PV1, was produced in limited quantities during the period 1920–5.

In the early thirties several attempts were made to lighten and improve the Maxim design to provide a suitable light automatic weapon capable of firing from a simple bipod, and two 'modified Maxims' were actually submitted for trial alongside the Degtyarev designed DP1926. The Maxim based designs were the products of that ubiquitous designer, Fedor Vassilyevich Tokarev (the weapon being called the Maxim-Tokarev or simply the MT) and of an engineer named Koleshnikov of whom little is known (called the Maxim-Koleshnikov, or MK). The former weapon, the MT, was an air-cooled type firing from a 250 round fabric belt and was issued in 1928 for limited trials. However so many complaints were received from the troops that the principal advantage of the weapon —that it could be produced on machinery formerly intended for the PM1910—was lost in the need for a complete redesign. As a result, the MT was abandoned and the surviving specimens were supposedly sold to the Spanish Loyalist forces for use in the Spanish Civil War—although a few were reportedly used by China between 1937 and 1945. Few details have ever been uncovered concerning the MT, which was a bipod fitted, lightened, Maxim with a semipistol grip stock. Even less is known about the MK, which was essentially similar to the MT except for its unusual pistol grip stock. Like the MT, the Kolesnikov design proved unsuited to service requirements and the surviving examples were sent to Spain.

An attempt had also been made in this period to modify the Maxim design to fire a 13mm round, but this also proved unsuccessful and few of these weapons were ever made, the only recorded delivery being that of eight to military educational establishments in the Moscow area.

Mention has already been made of the Degtyarev DP1926 light machine-gun design submitted as an alternative to the 'modified Maxims': the operating principles for this had been formulated in 1920–2 by Vasiliy Alexeyevich Degtyarev, although the idea had been originally expounded some five decades previously by Friberg. After four years' work Degtyarev submitted an experimental model for trial alongside the MT and MK and this prototype became known as the DP1926 (the 'P' representing *Pekhotniy* or 'Infantry'). During trials, however, some of the principal components of the operating mechanism failed including the mainspring, which had undergone an inadequate tempering process However, the two competing designs put on such a poor performance that the DP1926 was given a second chance to prove its worth, and in a second series of trials the Degtyarev design did indeed show considerable promise. As a result, a modified version of the DP1926 was issued to the forces on a limited scale along with two derivatives of the basic weapon; an aircraft gun called the DA was introduced in the same year and a tank gun, the DT followed in 1929. All were purely experimental models, however, and volume production did not begin until the mid thirties.

Various attempts were then made to modify the Degtyarev light machine-gun into a heavier gun capable of sustained firing from a tripod, the weapon to use a newly introduced 12·7mm cartridge. The first of these weapons, all of which were belt fed, was the DK1934—a gun little known outside Russia and one which only ever attained the status of prototype for the succeeding designs. The DK was equipped with the combined ground/anti-aircraft mounting much favoured by the Russians: in the ground role the gun was trundled around on two small wheels from which it could be readily converted for high-angle fire by discarding the axle unit and extending the trail into a shoulder-high tripod.

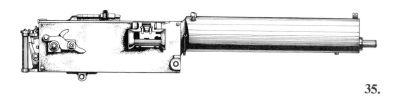

35.

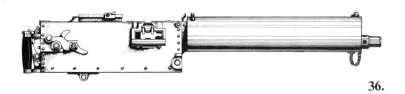

36.

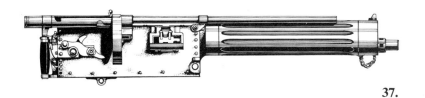

37.

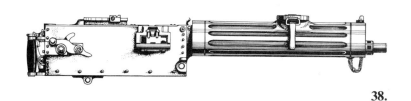

38.

35-38. *The development of the Russian Maxim machine-gun: plate 35 is the original PM1905, with a bronze water jacket; this was replaced by a plain steel casing in the PM1910 (36). Later weapons used a fluted casing (37— the weapon is shown with a sub-calibre training device attached), and the final version of the PM1910 (38) had a large water entry port.*

The DK proved abortive and was discarded, being followed within 4 years by the DShK 1938. This was designed by the joint talents of Vasiliy Degtyarev and Georgiy Shpagin (of submachine-gun fame), both designers being honoured in the gun's designation. The DShK proved eminently successful and continued in service throughout the war, a modified version (DShK 1938/46) being introduced after the cessation of hostilities. In 1939 yet another of the Degtyarev types was introduced—the ill-fated DS1939 medium machine-gun. The DS represented a considerable departure from the usual Soviet production methods in that it was intended to be a 'prestige' gun of far superior external finish to the other service weapons. The mechanism incorporated provision for the alteration of the cyclic rate to enable the gun to be economically used in both ground and anti-aircraft roles. Although this unit was of simple conception, and the weapon itself had relatively few moving parts, considerable operating trouble was encountered, which led to its being abandoned upon the introduction of the SG1943.

The SG1943 was the design of a talented engineer named Pyotr Maximovich Goryunov, who died in 1943 before finishing the task. His machine-gun was completed and perfected by his brother, Mikhail Goryunov, and an engineer named Voronkov. As usual, the Russians claimed that the SG43's operating mechanism was the result of Soviet technical knowledge—just as they have insisted that virtually every other invention of note was of Russian origin—but it has been proved that Goryunov's weapon was originally derived from a design registered in the American Patent Office by John M. Browning. However it still remains to Goryunov's credit that the gun was successfully transferred from paper to the production line in a very short period, and was still in service in 1969 (albeit in a modified form) with combat units of the Soviet army.

Besides those weapons intended for direct use in a ground role, the Russians sometimes converted the flexibly-mounted aircraft guns to ground support use. The most common of these modifications was that of the complicated ShKAS machine-gun either to a special anti-aircraft mount or occasionally to a tripod. The gun, the design of Boris Gabrielovich Shpitalny and Irnahr Andriyevich Komaritsky had undergone a number of design modifications since its inception in 1932. The most common of the ground support types were the KM35 and KM36 flexible designs, although an earlier model, the KM33, was used on a very limited scale; all these guns were characterised by an extremely high rate of fire—between 1,700 and 2,000 rpm, depending on the particular model. The heavier BS machine-gun, designed by Mikhail Beresin and firing a 12·7mm cartridge, was often used as secondary armament on Soviet armoured vehicles and for anti-aircraft defence.

The Russian forces also obtained a considerable amount of foreign material form various sources. Among those weapons known to have been used were the following types: Czechoslovakian ZB26 (7·92mm calibre); German MG08, MG08/15, MG13, MG34, MG42 (all 7·92mm); British Vickers and Vickers-Berthier (0·303in); American Browning M1917 (0·30in) Colt M1914 (7·62mm—the Russian rifle cartridge), Lewis (0·30in) and Maxim types (7·62mm).

Below. Two Soviet soldiers are shown making use of natural cover in the Urals, Autumn 1942. The soldier in the foreground has a DP1928 light machine-gun, while his companion has an M1891/30 rifle.

39.

39, 40. *7·62mm Machine-Gun, PM 1910*

The final development of the 'Russian Maxims': belt fed and water cooled, the PM1910 was operated on recoil principles. Like the British Vickers— itself a derivative of the Maxim— additional thrust was imparted to the recoiling breech block by trapping gases at the muzzle. Several PM1910 variants may be found, but the type was finalised with the addition of a large water entry port on top of the barrel jacket. The machine-gun was issued with two different types of mounting: the first, the ever-popular 'Sokolov' (so named after the designer), consisted of a wheeled carriage and a U shaped trail, although those of early manufacture had two extra legs to lift the wheels clear of the ground (plate 40). The 'Universal' mounting was a proper tripod; this, too, possessed wheels and the legs folded together to form a trail. Both mounts were sometimes fitted with a steel shield to protect the firer. The sights fitted to the PM1910 were a folding bar rearsight equipped with a sight aperture and a barleycorn foresight offset to the left to avoid the various water inlets. A bracket for an optical sight was occasionally fixed to the left side of the breech (visible in plate 40).

40.

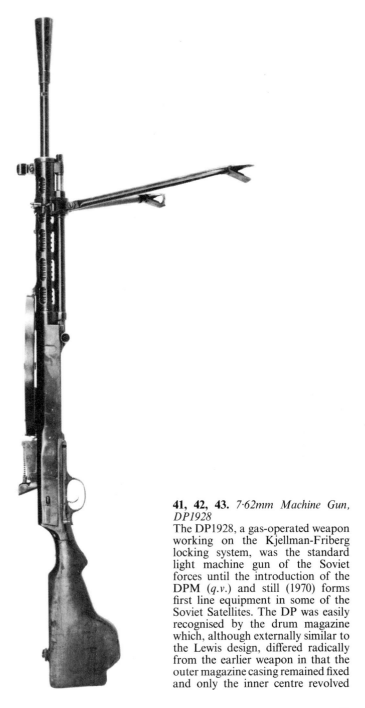

41, 42, 43. *7·62mm Machine Gun, DP1928*
The DP1928, a gas-operated weapon working on the Kjellman-Friberg locking system, was the standard light machine gun of the Soviet forces until the introduction of the DPM (*q.v.*) and still (1970) forms first line equipment in some of the Soviet Satellites. The DP was easily recognised by the drum magazine which, although externally similar to the Lewis design, differed radically from the earlier weapon in that the outer magazine casing remained fixed and only the inner centre revolved

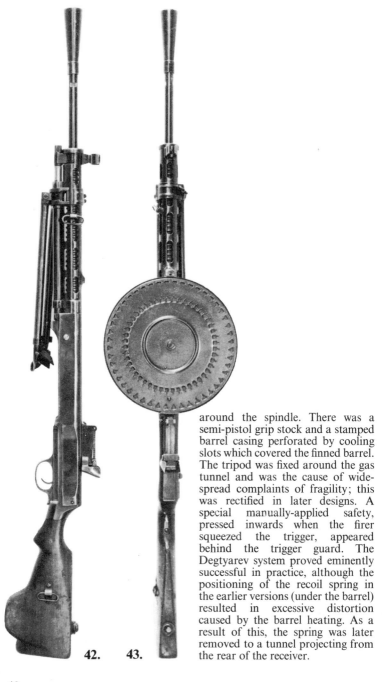

around the spindle. There was a semi-pistol grip stock and a stamped barrel casing perforated by cooling slots which covered the finned barrel. The tripod was fixed around the gas tunnel and was the cause of widespread complaints of fragility; this was rectified in later designs. A special manually-applied safety, pressed inwards when the firer squeezed the trigger, appeared behind the trigger guard. The Degtyarev system proved eminently successful in practice, although the positioning of the recoil spring in the earlier versions (under the barrel) resulted in excessive distortion caused by the barrel heating. As a result of this, the spring was later removed to a tunnel projecting from the rear of the receiver.

42.   43.

44, 45. *7·62mm Machine-Gun, DT 1929*

The DT was a modified version of the basic DP infantry gun intended to provide a weapon suitable for the secondary armament of armoured cars and tanks. The DT action was identical in operation to that of the DP, modifications being confined to external items: the wooden stock was replaced by a retractable metal stock and a wooden pistol grip, and a different drum magazine was used, holding 60 rounds in two tiers. A new aperture rearsight, rather than a tangent-leaf type, was often fitted when the gun was mounted on a bipod—when used as a tank-mounted gun (except in the anti-aircraft role), a separate optical sight was used.

44.   **45.**

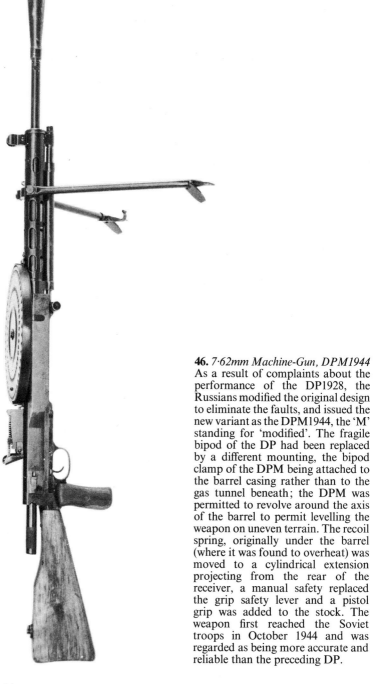

46. *7·62mm Machine-Gun, DPM1944*
As a result of complaints about the performance of the DP1928, the Russians modified the original design to eliminate the faults, and issued the new variant as the DPM1944, the 'M' standing for 'modified'. The fragile bipod of the DP had been replaced by a different mounting, the bipod clamp of the DPM being attached to the barrel casing rather than to the gas tunnel beneath; the DPM was permitted to revolve around the axis of the barrel to permit levelling the weapon on uneven terrain. The recoil spring, originally under the barrel (where it was found to overheat) was moved to a cylindrical extension projecting from the rear of the receiver, a manual safety replaced the grip safety lever and a pistol grip was added to the stock. The weapon first reached the Soviet troops in October 1944 and was regarded as being more accurate and reliable than the preceding DP.

47. *7·62mm Tank Machine-Gun, DTM1944*
The DTM1944 was modified from the improved DPM infantry weapon. Fitted with a retractable steel stock and a 60 round drum magazine, it was virtually identical to the DT1929 except for the positioning of the recoil spring cylinder at the rear of the receiver.

45

48. *7·62mm Machine-Gun, DS1939*
In 1939, a medium Degtyarev
designed machine-gun was introduced to replace the old Maxim
types. The DS1939, a scaled down
version of the DShK1938, was intended to be capable of sustained
automatic fire using the standard
Soviet rifle cartridge and feed from
a non-disintegrating belt rather than
a drum unit. The gun was immediately recognisable by its finned
barrel jacket and spade grips and
the trigger unit mounted on the
backplate. It had relatively few
moving parts. Provision for changing
the cyclic rate of fire was included,
the higher rate (1,100rpm) being
considered more suitable for anti-
aircraft work, and the lower (550rpm)
for the ground role: the rate of fire
could be quickly altered by changing
the size of the gas port aperture and
altering the tension in the buffer
spring. Difficulties encountered with
this system led to the DS being
abandoned in 1943. A convertible,
dual purpose, wheeled tripod mount
—sometimes shielded—was generally
used with this weapon in the infantry
role.

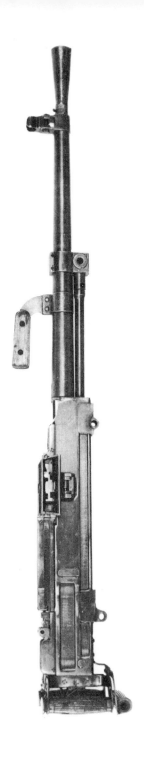

49. *7·62mm Machine-Gun, SG1943*
Another of the belt-fed Russian machine-guns, the SG was hastily introduced in 1943, after the failure of the DS1939. For the first time since the Maxim, the Russians departed from the ideas of Degtyarev and turned instead to the principles propounded by Goryunov; the former had used locking flaps on either side of the bolt unit and the latter's system cammed the rear of the whole bolt unit into the right side of the receiver wall; once again the designer relied upon gas operation to actuate the weapon. The external appearance of the SG was that of a slender belt fed weapon with spade grips and the trigger unit mounted on the backplate. The barrel was also devoid of any cooling fins (although in the post-war derivation, the SGM, the barrel was manufactured with a fluted barrel casing). Provision was made for a folding carrying handle and a conical flash hider was welded to the muzzle. The SG1943 was issued to the troops on a dual purpose ground/anti-aircraft mounting, equipped with wheels to ease its movement.

47

50, 51. *12·7mm Machine-Gun, DShK 1938*

The DShK remained the standard Soviet heavy machine-gun for the duration of the war; in addition to being the standard infantry gun, it was also used as the secondary armament on some of the larger armoured vehicles and on a number of the smaller naval patrol vessels. The gun was designed by the combined talents of Degtyarev and Shpagin, who contributed the locking mechanism and the feed unit respectively. A unique form of feed was used to provide the certainty and uniformity of feed expected from a drum unit allied with the capacity of a belt: a rotary block, protected by

52 *(above). The DShK1938 and tripod, with the tripod wheels dismounted.*

a steel stamping, was placed above the breech mechanism, the cartridges being stripped from the links in the belt, revolved around the block and indexed into the chamber. The locking mechanism was that of the standard Degtyarev infantry machine-gun, the DP1928, which cammed the bolt unit flaps in and out of the receiver walls. The external appearance of the DShK resembled that of the DS, with spade grips, the trigger unit mounted on the backplate, a barrel with cooling fins and a large muzzle brake/compensator welded to the muzzle. A standard pattern of leaf rearsight was normally fitted, but this was occasionally replaced by either the M1938 or M1941 anti-aircraft sights, both of which were suitable for firing at rapidly moving surface targets. Like the SG, a dual purpose ground and anti-aircraft mount was provided and two small wheels were issued to enable the unit to be easily moved; to convert this for AA fire, the wheels were removed and the trail extended to form a shoulder high tripod. An armoured shield was often provided, and the guns were occasionally used in double or quadruple anti-aircraft mounts occasionally in conjunction with a searchlight.

Anti-Tank Rifles

Owing to their propensity for close-quarter fighting the Russians were equipped with anti-tank rifles long after both their allies and their enemies had discarded them as obsolete. The reason for this has never been clear, since the armour penetrating capabilities of anti-tank rifles was strictly limited, and the performance of the Russian weapons was in no way better than that of their counterparts elsewhere. In fact only four such models were reported in service with the Red Army.

The first, which apparently lacks an official Russian designation but is often called 'Model 1938' was a single-shot bolt action weapon based very closely upon the German PzAGew 1918, a greatly enlarged bolt-actioned anti-tank weapon based on the standard German Gewehr 1898 infantry rifle. The Soviet derivation was 70·7in long with a 39·5in barrel and weighed 39lb 14oz with the bipod mount. It was reputed to have been altered in 1939 to provide a weapon firing from a five-round box magazine: this was 75·8in long overall (including the compensator/muzzle brake) with a barrel length of 45·6in, and weighed 43lb 15oz with the bipod. Both single-shot M1938 and its magazine successor were intended to use the same 12·7mm rimless round as the DShK1938 machine-gun, but both proved to be complete failures, tank armour having by then become too massive for the bullets to penetrate, and the rifles were hastily discarded.

The next designs to be introduced appeared concurrently in 1941, one designed by Simonov and the other by Degtyarev, magazine fed and single-shot respectively. Neither was much liked, partly because of the excessive weight and length, and partly because the design of the muzzle brake/compensator tended to direct the muzzle blast back into the firer's face. Although more efficient than most contemporary foreign designs the armour penetration of the two types was also relatively poor. A drawback that affected the autoloading Simonov design was that the gas port tended to clog in the extreme conditions of the bleak Russian winter, which meant that the gun could only be used as a single-shot weapon and had to be manually recocked after each shot. Nevertheless, this weapon was still in service at the end of the war—the fact that the infantry lacked a more effective anti-tank weapon remains a notable feature of Soviet wartime armament.

As well as these anti-tank rifles, the Russian infantry were also equipped with two designs of 76·2mm calibre infantry guns. The first of these, the 76·2mm Infantry Gun, M1927 L/16·5 was later replaced by the 76·2mm Infantry Gun, M1942 L/20: the latter weapon was much disliked owing to the very low muzzle velocity— 860 feet per second—which meant that even hollow charge ammunition was unable to penetrate the armour of the contemporary German tanks.

The Russians also made extensive use of anti-tank guns of various types and, indeed, they appear to have been the first power to recognize the race between gun and armour—at a time when other nations were standardizing on 37mm guns, the Russians were already issuing 45mm weapons. The principal anti-tank guns of the period were the 45mm M1937, the 45mm M1942, the 57mm M1941 and the 57mm M1943. The 76·2mm M1936 L/50 field-gun was also used with great effect against German armour, and a 100mm gun was introduced in 1944: most Soviet field-guns and howitzers below 152mm calibre were issued with armour piercing shot of some description, although the ammunition was rarely as efficient as contemporary foreign designs.

Below. A rather ambitious Soviet soldier is shown using a PTRS anti-tank rifle in an anti-aircraft role. This propagandist picture dates from early 1942.

52.   54.

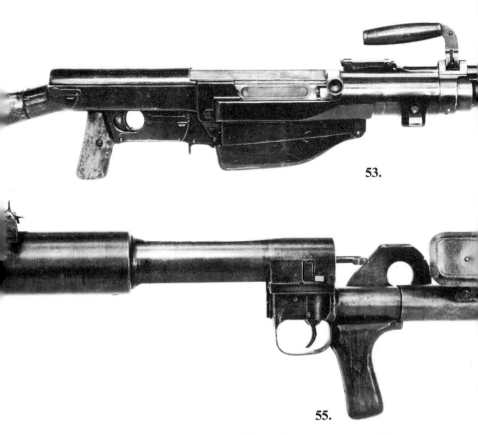

53.

55.

52, 54. *14·5mm Anti-tank Rifle, PTRS1941*
The PTRS was a gas-operated self-loading weapon using the 'hollow square' locking block of the AVS rifle; it was magazine fed, capacity being five rounds stripped from an asymmetrical clip which had to be loaded with the column of three cartridges on the right, otherwise the action remained inoperable. The gun had a wooden stock, a wooden pistol grip and a very long, detachable, barrel fitted with a muzzle brake and a bipod. There was an adjustable apeture to the gas port unit, and an above-barrel operating rod protected by a steel tube. The safety catch was located forward of the trigger guard on the right side.

53, 55. *14·5mm Anti-tank Rifle, PTRD1941*
The PTRD was a single shot bolt action weapon, locking being achieved through the action of two lugs on the bolt head engaging in recesses cut into the receiver wall. The cartridges were pushed home manually but the opening of the bolt, together with ejection and extraction, was actuated by recoil, when the bolt handle was forced up an inclined plate fixed to the right of the butt assembly where it was held while the moving parts returned to rest. The weapon was of all-metal construction and was provided with a carrying handle, a bipod and a muzzle brake; the safety 'hook' protruded from the rear of the bolt.

Mortars

Until 1936, all the Russian equipment of this nature had been of German or French origin obtained either during World War I or during the period of close Russo-German co-operation in the 1920s. In 1936, however, the Soviet authorities introduced the first of their indigenous types, the 82mm Mortar M1936—a close copy of the French Stokes-Brandt design, the M1917/31, which also formed the basis for the weapons of many other nations. Experiments were also begun at this time to produce a suitable type of 50mm unit, later culminating in the limited issue of the 50mm Mortar M1938 to the Russian troops. In 1937, an improved version of the 82mm battalion mortar, the 82mm M1937 had been introduced. Like the preceding design in this calibre, the 1937 type was not held in any high regard and achieved only a limited success. In the following year the Red Army was also issued with the first of the smaller 50mm varieties, the 50mm Mortar M1938; smooth-bored and bipod mounted, this weapon did not prove very successful and—together with a successor, the 50mm Mortar M1939—was quickly discarded. After this the 50mm Mortar M1940—which proved the first of a series of successful designs—was brought into service. This 1940 design was bipod mounted and could be fired only at two fixed quadrant elevations, 45° and 75°. Variations in range were accomplished by altering the rate of dissipation of the propelling gases through a valve at the base of the barrel. This mortar was to a large extent replaced by an improved and simplified design, the 50mm Mortar M1941, which dispensed with the bipod and shock absorbers while retaining the same operating principles as its predecessors. Also in 1941 the 82mm Mortar M1941 was introduced, a weapon easily recognised by its two stub axles with removable wheels mounted at the extremities of two short legs extending from the bottom of the elevating column. The latter feature was introduced as a direct result of the lessons gleaned during the campaigns in Finland, where the continual dismounting of the 82mm mortars then in service (1936 and 1937 patterns) for transportation proved unsatisfactory. Experience during the 1940–41 campaigns in Russia then decided the Russian designers to revert to a permanently-fixed mounting, so the last of the wartime models, the 82mm Mortar M1943, had light stamped wheels attached to a fixed axle.

The legs on the end of the elevating column held the wheels clear of the ground in the firing position.

Although only those mortars having a calibre less than 82mm could rightly be classed as infantry weapons, the Russians issued far larger varieties (107mm, 120mm and 160mm) to their specially-equipped artillery units.

Since they had always been artillery minded—and the mortar is truly a gunner's weapon—the Russians laid great emphasis on the use of their mortars. In an offensive role they were often employed en masse with devastating effect, leaving a profound impression with their opponents.

56.

57.

50mm Mortars M1938 and M1939
Little is known about these two weapons except that both were relatively conventional, gravity fired mortars, range being varied by changes in the gas dissipation rate. Both were bipod mounted, with smooth-bore barrels, and small oval baseplates: both could be fired only at fixed quadrant elevations. The ammunition was of standard finned bomb type, and only a primary charge could be used. Neither mortar lasted long in the Russian service.

56. *50mm Mortar, M1940*
This was a modification of the two earlier designs; the barrel was mounted on a circular, corrugated, pressed-steel baseplate and fitted with a simple stamped bipod upon which was mounted the elevating, traversing and cross-levelling gear. Two positions were provided for the sight, at 45° and 75°, a clinometer bubble being used to indicate when these elevations had been obtained. Range variations were effected by the rate

of gas dissipation past the firing pin holder, which acted as a mushroom valve.

57. *50mm Mortar, M1941*
The 1941 design was perhaps the most distinctive of all the Russian mortars, being immediately recognisable by the lack of any bipod and the unusually shaped baseplate unit. As with all of the 50mm designs, the M1941 fired only at two fixed quadrant angles, gas dissipation altering the range: in this design the gas dissipated through a valve formed by the barrel and the breech cap (with a fixed firing pin). A collar was threaded over both parts to form a gas tight seal and this item had gas exit ports communicating with an exhaust pipe; rotation of the collar moved the breech cap in relation to the ports and controlled the gas escape rate. Two levelling bubbles were mounted on the upper of the two cross levelling plates, thus dispensing with the need for clinometer bubbles on the sight.

56

58.

82mm Mortar, M1936
Little is known about this mortar, which was issued only on a very limited scale, beyond the fact that it was a conventional muzzle-loaded gravity fired weapon, elevated by means of a screw column attached to the bipod. It was quickly replaced by the M1937.

58. *82mm Mortar, M1937*
The M1937 was a modified version of the M1936. It was readily identifi-

able by its two small shock absorber cylinders which were replaced by a single long unit on the two later designs of 1941 and 1943. The base-plate was made from stampings and pressings crudely welded together, and was more complicated than those on the ensuing designs. Range adjustments were made by adjusting the elevating column height, or by adding further charge increments ('secondaries') to the primary propellant in the bomb itself.

59.

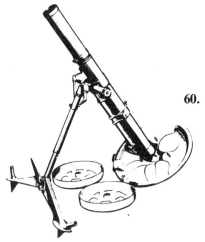

60.

59. *82mm Mortar, M1941*
Developed from the two earlier designs, the 1941 variety was fitted with a special bipod unit, capable of being fitted with two small wheels for easier travelling and to obviate the necessity for dismounting the barrel. The circular dished base-plate, characteristic of most of the larger Soviet mortars, was used and this had pronounced metal ribs welded to the underside. The weapon was gravity fired, range being altered either by altering the elevation or by adding secondary charges.

60. *82mm Mortar, M1943*
Virtually identical to the M1941, the 1943 type had two light pressed-steel wheels permanently fixed to an axle above the bipod legs. In the firing position, the weight was taken on the feet of the bipod, as the wheels were then lifted clear of the ground.

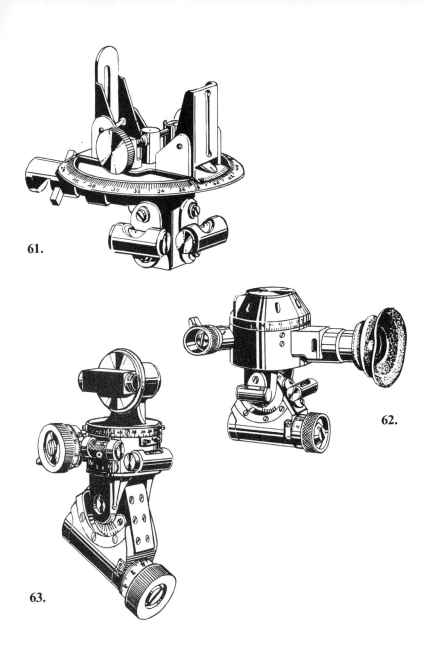

61.

62.

63.

61-3. *Mortar sights*
61, open sight used on 50mm and 82mm mortars; 62, MP1 optical sight used with 82mm mortars; 63, MP82 collimator sight used with mortars of calibre 82mm and above.

Grenades

The Russian troops were particularly fond of their grenades, which they often called 'pocket artillery'. In 1920 the Red Army was equipped with obsolete stick grenades dating in some cases from before the World War I. One of these types (the M1914) was the first grenade to be produced by the Soviets, albeit in a modified form, under the designation M1914/30. In the same year, quantities of a small rifle grenade, the VGD1930, were issued: this grenade necessitated the provision of a special rifled launcher which had to be fixed to the barrel of the rifle from which the grenade was to be fired. In 1933 another stick variety, the RGD1933—said to have been designed by Dyanokov—was produced to supplement the stocks of the M1914/30 conversion; this, like the earlier pattern, was a dual purpose hand-thrown weapon (capable of being used in both offensive and defensive roles). The Russians introduced their best fragmentation grenade, called the F1, sometime between 1937 and 1939: in external appearance it was similar to the British Mills Bomb, and proved to be reasonably efficient with good fragmentation properties.

None of these hand-thrown grenades were capable of immobilising a tank, but in the mid-thirties the Russian designers began experimenting with anti-tank grenades. Two models were introduced in 1940 as a result of their work: the RPG1940 and the VPGS1941. The former was a large 'potato masher' type, which was hand-thrown, but suffered from undistinguished armour penetration and was soon discarded. The more efficient VPGS was projected from a rifle, and introduced the 'shaped-charge' effect to the Russian service. By this time, however, many of the factories in which they were produced had been overrun in the rapid German advance of June 1941, and the next grenades, the RG1941 and the RTD1942, were very much simplified. Both designs consisted simply of explosive filled cylinders with concentric fragmentation liners. The last of the Russian grenades to see use in World War II was another of the 'shaped-charge' designs, the RPG1943, intended as a replacement for the RPG1940. It was stabilised by a conical fin trailing behind the grenade body on two fabric strips.

In general, the Russian grenades were reasonably effective, although their 'shaped-charge' was not the most efficient form.

Some of the types—the VPGS1941 and the VGD1930 being examples—were somewhat expensive to manufacture and in consequence their availability and use were limited. Some were of overcomplicated design, a fault which found little favour with the Russian authorities.

64. *Stick Grenade, M1914/30*
The M1914/30 grenade could be used either as an anti-personnel weapon (with a fragmentation jacket attached) or as a source of HE when the fragmentation unit was omitted. The grenade head held a safety catch, which retained the cocking piece, and a firing lever was built into the handle. The lever was held in place by a metal ring when not in use; when thrown, the delay fuze was activated by the lever flying open when the retaining ring was removed. The grenades were always supplied with separate detonators, which fitted into a recess in the head of the weapon.

65. *Rifle Projected Fragmentation Grenade, VGD1930*
The VGD grenade looked rather like an artillery shell with a fragment-ation jacket. A special rifled launcher, called the RM, was required to be fitted to the barrel of the rifle. Driving studs were fitted to the base of the bomb to engage rifling grooves and so impart spin to the missile. No safety device was provided, and there was no mechanical impact fuzing; the grenade could be fired by the standard ball cartridge, as the bullet could pass through an axial tube cut through the grenade. Several different explosive loadings were to be found.

61

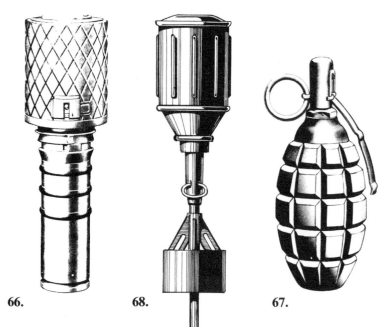

66.   **68.**   **67.**

66. *Stick grenade, M1933*
The 1933 grenade never entirely supplanted the earlier design. In common with the M1914/30, an optional fragmentation jacket could be used. The M1933 had a cylindrical handle which screwed onto the grenade head, and contained the complex firing mechanism; the head also had a recess for the fuze. The grenade was cocked by pulling the handle away from the head and then turning it to the right: the safety slide was then moved to the left, and the motion of throwing activated the fuze.

67. *Fragmentation Grenade, F1*
The F1 grenade had a cast-iron body, serrated for fragmentation. The fuze assembly—similar to that employed on the RTD1942—screwed into the grenade body and there was a conventional ring and split-pin holding the lever to the body. The weapon was detonated by withdrawing the split pin, pulling the ring away from the grenade and then throwing. The lever came away from the body, allowed the striker to descend onto the firing cap and ignited the delay fuze. The F1 had good fragmentation properties, the splinters being hurtled up to 30 yards from the point of impact.

68. *Rifle Projected Anti-tank Stick Grenade, VPGS1941*
This grenade had a hollow 'shaped-charge' head, and a long rod extending rearwards from the body. When fired, the fin unit slipped down the rod and locked into place in a groove cut at the tip. This served the purpose of stabilising the grenade and also permitted it to strike the target head first. An impact fuze was provided.

62

69. *Anti-tank Stick Grenade, RPG 1940*
The RPG consisted of a cylindrical head containing the explosive charge and a handle containing both the safety system and an impact fuze. As with most of the Russian grenades, the detonator was separately supplied, and was fitted into a cavity in the head of the weapon.

70. *Grenade RG1941*
The RG grenade depended for its effect on a combination of fragmentation and blast; the body of the grenade, a cylindrical container, held the explosive charge and three concentric fragmentation 'liners'. The 'lid' contained the firing mechanism, and the safety lever was retained in the locked position by a pin, to which was attached a fabric loop. When the loop was pulled, the lever could be released and the grenade was then thrown.

71. *Grenade, RTD1942*
A simplified version of the RG1941, the RTD consisted of a cylinder containing a TNT fitting and the fragmentation liners. The fuze unit was virtually identical to that of the F1, removal of the pin permitting the safety lever to spring out and allowing the striker to hit the cap. The fuze assembly had to be fitted before use, a wooden stopper and metal cap being used to plug the fuze cavity prior to this operation.

72. *Anti-tank Stick Grenade, RPG 1943*
The 1943 design was introduced to replace the RPG1940, which was found to have poor armour penetration. The cylindrical head contained a 'shaped charge' and the wooden handle held the safety lever. A conical sleeve was fixed to the handle; when thrown, this trailed behind the grenade on the ends of two long fabric strips, stabilising the grenade's flight and allowing it to strike in a head-on attitude.

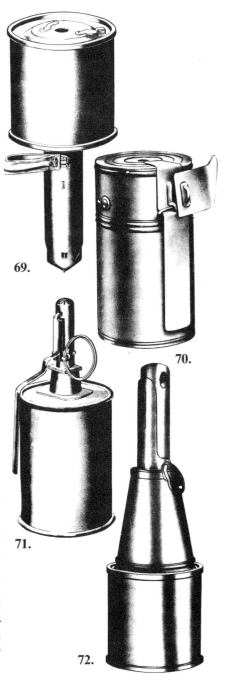

69.

70.

71.

72.

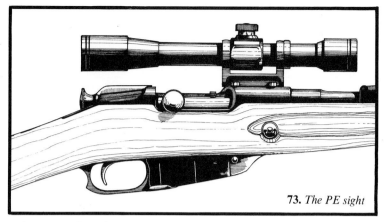

73. *The PE sight*

Telescopic Rifle Sights
Two telescopic sights were in general use among the Soviet snipers of World War II: the PE and the PU types. The PU was the smaller of the two designs, and saw widespread use during the war, but, because of a slight disadvantage described later, gradually lost favour with Soviet troops and, by the end of the war, had largely been replaced by the bigger PE sight. Owing to the short length of the smaller telescope, and fact that the unit was mounted above the receiver ring, the firer had to crane forward to adjust his sights for every change in target, because of this, the Soviet riflemen came to prefer the heavier PE type, which also had a greater magnification. Both sights were adjustable internally for windage and elevation, suitably cali-

brated knobs appearing on the telescope barrel. The PE variation was sighted to 1,400 metres and the PU to 1,300; the reticule consisted of a tapered-tip post and cross-hairs.

Several different mountings were developed for these sights, which were generally fitted to the standard Mosin-Nagant M1891/30 rifle. Either two ring mounts were fixed to brackets dovetailed to the receiver, or a one-piece mount was placed in a dovetailed slot on the left hand side of the weapon. A special pressed-steel mounting was developed for the SVT1938 and SVT1940 rifles in which the telescope was held over the rear of the weapon's action by a swept forward mount affixed to dovetailed slots in the rear of the receiver itself. Only the smaller PU sight was used in conjunction with this unit.

74. *The PU sight*

Ammunition

In general terms, the ammunition issued to the Russian armed forces was of inferior quality to that of the other major powers, particularly those rounds made in Russia before 1930.

The smallarms ammunition was divided into seven dissimilar types:

    i)   7·62mm Nagant revolver ammunition

    ii) 7·62mm Tokarev pistol and sub-machinegun ammunition

    iii) 7·62mm Mosin-Nagant rifle ammunition, which was also used in many of the Russian machine-guns

    iv) 7·62mm ShKAS machine-gun ammunition

    v)   12·7mm heavy machine-gun ammunition

    vi) 12·7mm ShVAK heavy machine-gun ammunition

    vii) 14·5mm anti-tank rifle ammunition

The rounds for the M1895 Nagant revolver had rimmed cases—although late examples manufactured under the Soviet régime were sometimes of steel, coated with gilding metal. The bullet, which was contained entirely within the cartridge case, had a lead core contained within a coated steel envelope. The propellant was flake nitrocellulose, although many of the rounds made before 1922 were loaded with black powder: in 1922, the Russian Arsenals began to manufacture their own supplies of nitrocellulose propellant.

The round designed for the TT1930 automatic pistol was based closely on the 7·63mm Mauser cartridge—and, indeed, the two are interchangeable. Several different loads are known to exist, including a tracer round known as the P41. A cartridge was also developed to test the qualities of steel helmets; these can be recognized by a khaki tipped roundnosed bullet. The cases for pistol and sub-machinegun ammunition are rimless and bottlenecked, made of brass or coated steel.

The 7·62mm 'rifle' round—originally intended for the Mosin-Nagant rifle but later adopted for the DP, DPM and SG machine-guns—existed in a bewildering variety of types, including light (Type L, or M1908) and heavy (Type D, or M1930) ball loads, armour-piercing (two types—one as yet unidentified, the other Type B30, M1930), armour-piercing-incendiary (API—Type BS40, M1940), armour-piercing-tracer (APT), armour-piercing-tracer-incendiary (APTI—Type BZT), high explosive incendiary (HEI—

Type ZP) as well as various 'special purpose' loads including grenade blanks, dummy, practice and silenced rounds. All these cartridges used bottlenecked rimmed cases about 54mm long; as a result, the cartridge is invariably known as the '7·62 × 54Rmm Mosin-Nagant'. The cartridge cases were originally made from brass, but steel was extensively used during the Great Patriotic War. These steel cases were coated either with gilding metal or with a wash of copper.

The ShKAS machine-gun used a round identical and external appearance to the rifle cartridge; a larger propellant charge was used to actuate the complex mechanism of the ShKAS. This ammunition should never be used in a rifle or in a different variety of machine-gun as there is considerable risk of damage—particularly to extractors—owing to the extra strain involved in firing the special ammunition. The ShKAS rounds are distinguished by the addition of the Cyrillic character Щ to the headstamp.

Two varieties of 12·7mm round were made, a rimmed version— intended for an unsuccessful 12·7mm derivative of the ShVAK aircraft cannon—which was quickly discarded, and a rimless version. The latter was extensively manufactured for the DShK 1938 and Beresin machine-guns in high-explosive-incendiary, armour-piercing and armour-piercing-incendiary loadings amongst others.

The two anti-tank rifles, the PTRS1941 and the PTRD1941, fired a 14·5mm calibre rimless cartridge which—like both the 12·7mm rounds—was bottlenecked.

Towards the end of the war the Russians began development of a 7·62mm 'intermediate' round inspired by German experimentation in a similar field. No weapon chambered for this cartridge (called the M1943 or the 7·62 × 39mm) appeared before 1945.

75.   76.

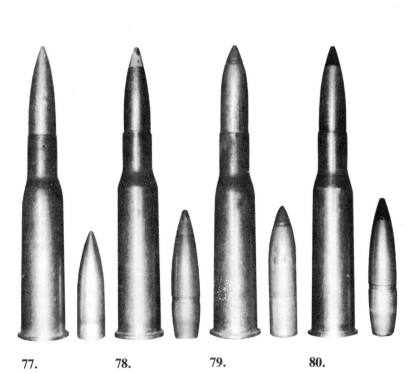

77.   78.   79.   80.

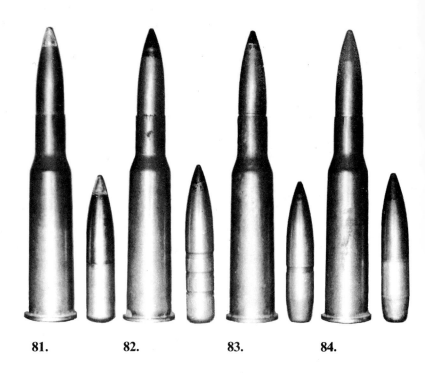

81.   **82.**   **83.**   **84.**

75. 7·62mm TT automatic pistol and submachine-gun round, together with a typical roundnosed ball removed from the case. 76. 7·62mm M1895 (Nagant) revolver round together with a sectioned specimen showing the bullet contained entirely within the cartridge case. 77. 7·62mm Type L (M1908) light ball round and bullet. 78. 7·62mm Type D (M1930) heavy ball round and bullet: yellow tipped. 79. 7·62mm armour-piercing round dating from the World War I and bullet: copper capped. 80. 7·62mm Type B30 (M1930) armour-piercing round and bullet: black tipped. 81. 7·62mm Type T tracer round and bullet: green tipped. 82. 7·62mm Type BZT armour-piercing-tracer-incendiary round and bullet: mauve tipped with a red band beneath. 83. 7·62mm Type B32 (M1932) armour-piercing-incendiary round and bullet: black tipped with a red band beneath. 84. 7·62mm Type ZP high-explosive-incendiary round and bullet: red tipped. 85. 12·7mm Type B32 (M1932) armour-piercing-incendiary round and bullet: black tipped with a red band beneath. The bullet on the right is for the 12·7mm Type BZT armour-piercing-tracer-incendiary round: mauve tipped with traces of a red band beneath. 86. 14·5mm Type B32 (M1932) armour-piercing-incendiary round and bullet: black tipped with a red band beneath.

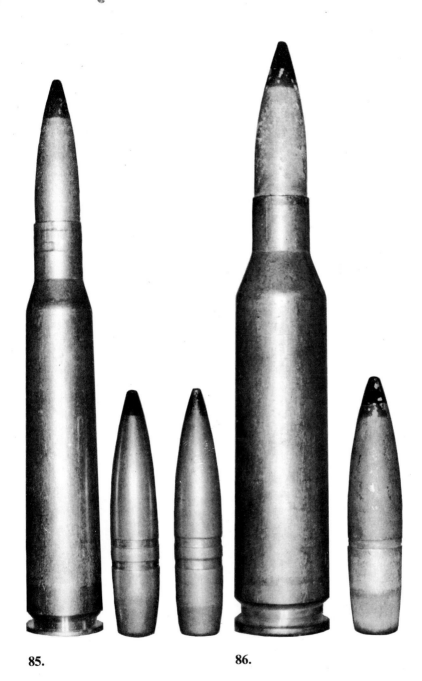

85.

86.

AMMUNITION DATA

Designation	Assembled Cartridge weight (grains)	length (mm)	Bullet weight (grains)	length (mm)	Propellant type	weight (grains)	Case length (mm)	Markings
M1895 Revolver								
7·62mm Ball R	202	38·7[1]	106	16·5	NC flake[2]	N	38·7[1]	
Automatic pistol and Submachine-gun								
7·62mm Ball P	167	34·6	85	14·3	NC flake	10	24·8	
7·62mm Tracer	160*	34·6	85*	N	NC flake	10*	24·8	Green tipped bullet
7·62mm API P–41	155	34·7	74	N	NC flake	10*	24·8	Black tipped bullet with red band beneath
7·62mm Helmet test	160*	34*	85*	14·0*	NC flake	10*	24·8	Khaki tipped bullet (roundnose)
Rifle and Machine-Gun[4,5]								
7·62mm Ball M1891	350	150	150	30·0*	Black powder[3]	N	53·6	
7·62mm Ball L (M1908)	350	76·9	148	29·0	NC cyl	50	53·6	Yellow tipped bullet
7·62mm Ball D (M1930)	380	76·9	182	33·3	NC cyl	46	53·6	Green tipped bullet
7·62mm Tracer T (M1930)	348	76·7	148	37·6	NC cyl	43·5	53·6	Copper capped bullet
7·62mm AP (pre 1930)	365	76·9	167	35·0	NC cyl	45·5	53·6	Black tipped bullet
7·62mm AP B–30 (M1930)	375	76·9	170	36·5	NC cyl	48	53·6	Black tipped bullet with red band beneath
7·62mm API B–32 (M1932)	371	76·8	155	37·0	NC cyl	50	53·6	Bullet and casemouth red, black tipped bullet and black casehead
7·62mm API BS–40 (M1940)	385	76·7	187	30·6	NC cyl	49	53·6	
7·62mm APT BT	357	77·0	158	40·1	NC cyl	49	53·6	Purple tipped bullet
7·62mm APTI BZT	360	76·8	142	40·6	NC cyl	49	53·6	Purple tipped bullet with red band beneath
7·62mm HEI ZP	375	76·8	156	38·9	NC cyl	44	53·6	Red tipped bullet and red primer
7·62mm Low velocity ball	302	76·7	149	33·3	NC cyl	7·5	53·6	Bullet, casehead and casemouth green (pre 1941)
7·62mm Practice ball	233	60*	69	N	NC cyl	12·5	53·6	Green tipped bullet and primer (post 1941)
7·62mm Grenade blank	175	53·6	NA	NA	NC cyl	23·2	53·6	No bullet, crimped casemouth
Heavy Machine-gun[6]								
12·7mm AP B30 (M1930)	2,156	146·9	800	63·5	NC tub	275	107·1	Black tipped bullet
12·7mm API B32 /M1932)	2,058	146·4	715	63·5	NC tub	255	107·1	Black tipped bullet with red band beneath
12·7mm APIT BZT	2,049	146·9	675	63·5	NC tub	265	107·1	Purple tipped bullet with red band beneath
12·7mm API BZ	2,088	146·7	741	64·2	NC tub	232	107·1	Black bullet tip with yellow band beneath
12·7mm HEI ZP	1,945	146·4	685	56·9	NC tub	255	107·1	Brass nose fuze
Anti-tank rifle								
14·5mm API B32 (M1932)	3,618	155·2	980	66·5	NC tub	469	131·8	Black tipped bullet with red band beneath
14·5mm API BS41 (M1941)	3,655	155·2	983	49·2	NC tub	485	131·8	Bullet varnished red with black tip and black primer

* approximately; NC cyl, cylindrical nitrocellulose; NC tub, tubular nitrocellulose; N, not known; [1] bullet contained within cartridge case; NA, not applicable; N, not applicable. [2] black powder prior to 1925 in Russian loadings; [3] some rounds were loaded with nitrocellulose; [4] dummy rounds and various types of blank may be encountered; [5] ammunition with the Cyrillic character III on the casehead was for the ShKAS machine-gun only; [6] a rimmed version of the 12·7mm round was used in the 12·7mm ShVAK aircraft machine-gun, issued only in very small numbers.

Data Tables

The tables on the following pages give basic details of all the more important Imperial and Soviet smallarms described in this book. One detail is not given—rifling—as it was common to all the weapons firing 7·62mm ammunition whether they were pistols, revolvers or submachine-guns. The barrels of these guns were bored with four grooves, of right hand twist, and having one turn in 31·33 calibres (9·4 inches): despite the differences in shape, size, and ballistic performance of the various 7·62mm projectiles, few complaints were ever recorded. The heavier weapons, the 12·7mm DShK 1938 and the 14·5mm PTRS 1941 and PTRD 1941 had eight groove rifling with a right hand twist.

In the tables the use of **N** represents a figure or feature unknown to the authors, and **NA** is used as an abbreviation for 'not applicable'. Other comments are given in the form of footnotes to the relevant table.

Table 1: PISTOLS AND REVOLVERS   ANTI-TANK RIFLES

DESIGNATION	M1895	TT1930, TT1933	TK	PTRS1941	PTRD1941
Designers	L. Nagant E. Nagant	F. V. Tokarev	? Korovin	S. G. Simonov	V. A. Degtyarev
Period of manufacture	1895–1914 (Belgian) c. 1900–1944 (Russian)	1930–1950 (?)	c. 1930–5	c. 1941–4	c. 1941–3
Operating system	Nagant	modified Browning	—	Simonov	N
Operating agent	manual	recoil	blowback	gas	manual
Locking system	pawl on ratchet and cylinder hand	lugs on barrel locking into slide recesses	—	vertically moving block	bolt action; 2 lugs on bolthead
Feed type	cylinder	box magazine	box magazine	dip loaded box	single shot
Capacity of feed unit	7	8	7		
Calibre (in/mm)	0·300/7·62	0·300/7·62	0·25/6·35	0·57/14·5	0·57/14·5
Length (in/mm)	9·06/230	7·68/195	about 5/127	83·8/2129	79·1/2009
Barrel length (in/mm)	4·35/110	4·56/116	about 2·5/64	48·3/1227	48·3/1227
Weight (lb/kg)	1·0/0·45[1]	2·04/0·91[2]	1·07/0·46[2]	45·9/20·8	38·2/17·3
Foresight	blade	blade	blade	pillar in cylindrical guard	blade
Rearsight	fixed U	fixed U	fixed U	leaf, 100–1500m	rectangular notch: 2 settings— below/above 600m
Type of fire	double- or single-action	self-loading	self-loading	self-loading	single shot
Muzzle velocity (fps/mps)	892/272	1377/542	820/250	3320/1012	3320/1012
Effective rate of fire (rpm)	14[3]	24[3]	21[3]	15	8
Effective range (yds/m)	55/50	55/50	22/20	880/800 (against bunkers)	880/800 (against bunkers)

[1] unloaded
[2] loaded
[3] assuming magazine has to be manually reloaded

Table 2: RIFLES

DESIGNATION	M1891	M1891 DRAGOON	M1910 CARBINE	M1891/30
Designers	S. I. Mosin L. Nagant E. Nagant	S. I. Mosin L. Nagant E. Nagant	S. I. Mosin L. Nagant E. Nagant	S. I. Mosin L. Nagant E. Nagant
Period of manufacture	1891–1930[1]	1900(?)–17[1]	1910–17[1]	1930–40(?)
Operating system	Mosin-Nagant	Mosin-Nagant	Mosin-Nagant	Mosin-Nagant
Operating agent	manual operation	manual operation	manual operation	manual operation
Locking system	turning lugs on bolt head	turning lugs on bolt head	turning lugs on bolt head	turning lugs on bolt head
Feed type	box (non-detachable)	box (non-detachable)	box (non-detachable)	box (non-detachable)
Capacity of feed unit	5	5	5	5
Calibre (in/mm)	0·300/7·62	0·300/7·62	0·300/7·62	0·300/7·62
Length (in/mm)	51·4/1306	48·8/1240	40·1/1019	48·5/1232
Barrel length (in/mm)	31·6/801	28·8/732	20·0/508	28·7/728
Weight (lb/kg)	9·6/4·4	8·8/4·0	7·5/3·4	8·7/3·9
Foresight	open barleycorn	open barleycorn	open barleycorn	guarded pillar
Rearsight	leaf to 2700 arshins	leaf to 2700 arshins	leaf to 2000 arshins	Tangent 100–2000m
Type of fire	single shot manually reloaded	single shot manually reloaded	single shot manually reloaded	single shot manually reloaded
Muzzle velocity (fps/mps)	2845/867	2810/856	2655/808	2800/853
Effective rate of fire (rpm)	10	10	10	10
Effective range (yds/m)	550/500	550/500	440/400	550/500

[1] some assembled from parts after the revolution, and dated 1918–1922

RIFLES—continued

DESIGNATION	M1938 CARBINE	M1944 CARBINE	AVS1936	SVT1938	SVT1940
Designers	S. I. Mosin, L. Nagant, E. Nagant	S. I. Mosin, L. Nagant, E. Nagant	S. G. Simonov	F. V. Tokarev	F. V. Tokarev
Period of manufacture	1938–1943	1944–7(?)	1936–7	1938–40	1940–44
Operating system	Mosin-Nagant	Mosin-Nagant	Simonov	Tokarev	Tokarev
Operating agent	manual operation	manual operation	gas	gas	gas
Locking system	turning lugs on bolt head	turning lugs on bolt head	vertically moving block	rear of bolt cammed down	rear of bolt cammed down
Feed type	box (non-detachable)	box (non-detachable)	box	box	box
Capacity of feed unit	5	5	15	10	10
Calibre (in/mm)	0·300/7·62	0·300/7·62	0·300/7·62	0·300/7·62	0·300/7·62
Length (in/mm)	40·1/1019	40·2/1021	48·6/1234	48·1/1222	48·1/1222
Barrel length (in/mm)	20·0/508	20·3/516	24·2/615	25·0/635	24·6/225
Weight (lb/kg)	7·7/3·4	8·2/3·7	8·9/4·04	8·7/3·95	8·6/3·90
Foresight	guarded pillar	guarded pillar	pillar	guarded pillar	guarded pillar
Rearsight	Tangent 100–1000m	Tangent 100–1000m	Leaf 100–1500m	Tangent leaf 100–1000m	Tangent 100–1500m
Type of fire	single shot manually reloaded	single shot manually reloaded	selective	self-loading	self-loading
Muzzle velocity (fps/mps)	2655/808	2655/808	2715/828	2725/831	2720/829
Effective rate of fire (rpm)	10	10	80[1]	30	30
Effective range (yds/m)	440/400	440/400	550/500	550/500	550/500

[1] automatic fire

Table 3: SUBMACHINE-GUNS

DESIGNATION	PPD1934/38	PPD1940	PPSh1941	PPS1943
Designers	V. A. Degtyarev	V. A. Degtyarev	G. S. Shpagin	V. Sudarev
Period of manufacture	1938–40	1940–41	1941–46(?)	1943–7(?)
Operating system	Bergmann	Bergmann	Bergmann	Bergmann
Operating agent	case projection ('blowback')	case projection	case projection	case projection
Locking system	NA	NA	NA	NA
Feed type	a) drum b) box	drum	a) drum b) box	box
Capacity of feed	a) 71 b) 25	71	a) 71 b) 35	35
Calibre (in/mm)	0·300/7·62	0·300/7·62	0·300/7·62	0·300/7·62
Length (in/mm)		30·6/777	33·2/843	35·75/908
Barrel length (in/mm)	10·6/269	10·6/269	10·6/269	10·0/254
Weight without mag. lb/kg	7·6/3·5	8·1/3·7	7·7/3·5	7·4/3·4
With full mag. lb/kg	11·5/5·2	11·7/5·3	12·0/5·4	8·6/3·9
Foresight	blade	blade	blade	blade
Rearsight	tangent leaf, graduated 0–500m	idem	tangent leaf, graduated 0–500m or rocking L 100m and 200m	rocking L 100m and 200m
Type of fire	selective	selective	selective	automatic
Muzzle velocity (fps/mps)	1640/500	1640/500	1640/500	1608/489
Cyclic rate (rpm)	800±50	800±50	950±50	600±40
Effective rate of fire	100	100	100	100
Effective range (yds/m)	220/200	220/200	220/200	220/200

Table 4: MACHINE GUNS

DESIGNATION	DP1928	DT1929	DPM1944	DTM1944
Designers	V. A. Degtyarev	V. A. Degtyarev	V. A. Degtyarev	V. A. Degtyarev
Period of manufacture	1928–44[1]	1929–44[1]	1944–7(?)	1944–7(?)
Operating system	modified Kjellman-Friberg	modified Kjellman-Friberg	modified Kjellman-Friberg	modified Kjellman-Friberg
Operating agent	gas	gas	gas	gas
Locking system	flaps on bolt unit	flaps on bolt unit	flaps on bolt unit	flaps on bolt unit
Feed type	drum	drum	drum	drum
Capacity of feed (rounds)	47[2]	60	47	60
Calibre (in/mm)	0·300/7·62	0·300/7·62	0·300/7·62	0·300/7·62
Length (in/mm)	49·8/1265	46·5/1181[3]	49·8/1265	46·5/1181[3]
Barrel length (in/mm)	23·8/605	23·5/597	23·8/605	23·5/597
Weight (lb/kg)	26·3/11·9	27·8/12·6	26·8/12·2	28·4/12·9
Weight of mount (if separate) (lb/kg)	NA	NA	NA	NA
Foresight	guarded pillar	guarded pillar	guarded pillar	guarded pillar
Rearsight	Tangent leaf 100–1500m	Apeture or Tangent leaf	Tangent leaf 100–1500m	Tangent leaf or Aperture
Type of fire	automatic	automatic	automatic	automatic
Muzzle velocity (fps/mps)	2770/844	2755/839	2770/844	2755/839
Cyclic rate (rpm)	550±30	600	550±30	600
Effective rate of fire (rpm)	80	125	80	125
Effective range (yds/m)	880/800	880/800	880/800	880/800

[1] in quantity only after 1935
[2] originally held 49, the quantity was reduced to avoid feeding troubles with loaded magazine
[3] stock extended

MACHINE GUNS – *continued*

DESIGNATION *Designers*	DS1939 V. A. Degtyarev	SG1943 P. M. Goryunov M. M. Goryunov I. Voronkov	PM1910 H. S. Maxim (originally)	DShK1938 V. A. Degtyarev G. S. Shpagin
Period of manufacture	1939–42	1943–8(?)	1910–45	1938–46
Operating system	modified Kjellman-Friberg	Goryunov	Maxim	modified Kjellman-Friberg
Operating agent	gas	gas	gas assisted recoil	gas
Locking system	flaps on bolt unit	laterally, swinging bolt unit	toggle joint	flaps on bolt unit
Feed type	metallic link belt	metallic link belt	fabric belt	metallic link belt[4]
Capacity of feed (rounds)	50	50	250	50
Calibre (in/mm)	0·300/7·62	0·300/7·62	0·300/7·62	0·500/12·7
Length (in/mm)	46·1/1171	44·1/1120	43·6/1107	62·3/1602
Barrel length (in/mm)	28·4/721	28·3/719	28·4/721	39·4/1002
Weight (lb/kg)	26·4/12·0	30·4/13·8	52·5/23·8	73·5/33·3
Weight of mount (if separate) (lb/kg)	N	59·3/26·9	99·6/45·2[5] 110·0/49·9[5]	313·2/142·1
Foresight	guarded pillar	blade or guarded pillar	barleycorn	guarded pillar
Rearsight	Tangent leaf 0–2400m	Tangent 0–2300m	various, see p. 40	Tangent leaf 200–3500m
Type of fire	automatic	automatic	automatic	automatic
Muzzle velocity (fps/mps)	2830/863	2830/863	2830/863	2765/843
Cyclic rate (rpm)	550±30 1100±80	580±80	550±30	580±30
Effective rate of fire (rpm)	100–200	125	125	125
Effective range (yds/m)	880/800	880/800	880/800	1650/1500

4 may be joined together to form a 250rd belt. The normal type has non-disintegrating metallic links, but a fabric belt may sometimes be found
5 depending on type of mount used

Table 5: MORTARS

DESIGNATION	50mm 1938	50mm 1940	50mm 1941	82mm 1941
Calibre (in/mm)	1·97/50	1·97/50	1·97/50	3·23/82
Weight (travelling) (lb/kg)	34·0/15·4	25·3/11·5	26·5/12·0	111/50·3[3]
Weight (firing) (lb/kg)	26·6/12·1	21·3/9·7	22·0/10·0	99·2/45·0
Weight (Barrel) (lb/kg)	8·3/3·8	8·25/3·7	9·0/4·1	42·9/19·5[4]
Weight (Baseplate) (lb/kg)	12·8/5·8	5·5/2·5	13·0/5·9	41·9/19·0[4]
Weight (Wheels) (lb/kg)	NA	NA	NA	45·2/20·5
Bore length (in/mm)	21·7/553	21·0/533	22·0/559[5]	48·0/1219
Baseplate dia (in/mm)	7·0 × 10·5/178 × 267[1]	10·0/254	10·3 × 17·0/262 × 432[2]	23·0/584
Type of ignition	gravity	gravity	gravity	gravity
No. of secondaries (max)	none	none	none	6
Max muzzle velocity (fps/mps)	315/96	315/96	315/96	692/211
Elevation	30° and 60°	45° and 75°	45° and 75°	45°–85°
Traverse (without moving bipod)	6°	9° at 45° / 16° at 75°	9° at 45° / 16° at 75°	6°
Range max. (yds/m) / min. (yds/m)	770/700 / 77/70	880/800 / 66/60	880/800 / 110/100	3300/3000 / 77/70
Max rate of fire (bombs per min)	30	30	30	25

[1] oval baseplate
[2] rectangular baseplate
[3] towed
[4] carried
[5] maximum range

Table 6: GRENADES

DESIGNATION *Type*	M1914/30 hand thrown dual purpose stick grenade	RGD1933 hand thrown dual purpose stick grenade	F1 hand thrown fragmentation grenade	RG1941 hand thrown fragmentation grenade[2]	RTD1942 hand thrown fragmentation grenade[2]
Explosive type/ (colour of grenade head)	Trinitrotoluene (TNT)	TNT	TNT	TNT	TNT
Overall length (in/mm)	9·3/236	7·5/191	4*/102*	N	4·6/117
Head diameter (in/mm)	1·8/46	2·2/56	2·5*/64*	N	2·2/56
Weight (oz/gm)	21/595	18/510	20/567[3]	14/397	15/425
Weight of fragmentation jacket (oz/gm)	8/227	8/277	NA	NA	NA
Weight of explosive (oz/gm)	N	N	1·6/46	N	3·9/111
Muzzle velocity (fps/mps)	NA	NA	NA	NA	NA
Approximate thrown range (yd/m)	44/40	44/40	44/40	55/50	55/50
Effective blast radius (yd/m) *with jacket* *without jacket*	27/25 11/10	27/25 11/10	16/15 NA	16/15 NA	22/20 NA
Armour penetration (in/mm)	NA	NA	NA	NA	NA
Delay type	fixed	fixed	fixed	fixed	fixed
Delay period sec.	4·3±0·7	3·6±0·4	4·0±0·5	3·5±0·3	3·7±0·7

GRENADES – continued

DESIGNATION	RPG1940	RPG1943	VGD1930	VPGS1941
Type	hand thrown anti-tank grenade	hand thrown anti-tank grenade	rifle launched fragmentation grenade	rifle launched anti-tank grenade
Explosive type/ (colour of grenade head)	TNT	TNT	Amatol (yellow) Ammonal (brown) Melinite (green) Scheiderite (red) Trotyl (grey)	Melinite (green) TNT (none) Trotyl (grey)
Overall length (in/mm)	7·9/201	8*/203*	4·5/114	18·2/463
Head diameter (in/mm)	3·8/97	3·8*/97*	1·6/41	2·4/61
Weight (oz/gm)	42/1191	44/1247	12/340	24/680
Weight of fragmentation jacket (oz/gm)	NA	NA	NA	NA
Weight of explosive (oz/gm)	N	N	1·7/48	N
Muzzle velocity (fps/mps)	NA	NA	175/53·4[4]	N
Approximate thrown range (yd/m)	22/20	22/20	330/300[4]	66/60
Effective blast radius (yd/m) with jacket without jacket	27/25 NA	NA NA	16/15 NA	NA NA
Armour penetration (in/mm)	1·2/30	3·0/75	NA	1·2/30
Delay type	[1]	[1]	variable	[1]
Delay period sec.	[1]	[1]	3·0-11·5	[1]

* approximately
[1] impact fuzed
[2] internal fragmentation jacket
[3] with fuze
[4] without booster charge, with this in operation MV = 360 fps (110 mps) range = 990 yd (900m)